EMILE BERLINER

Maker of the Microphone

By

FREDERIC WILLIAM WILE

Author of

Men Around the Kaiser
The Assault, Explaining the Britishers, Etc.

ILLUSTRATED

INDIANAPOLIS
THE BOBBS-MERRILL COMPANY
PUBLISHERS

Printed in the United States of America

PRINTED AND BOUND
BY BRAUNWORTH & CO., INC.
BROOKLYN, NEW YORK

To
THE YOUTH OF AMERICA

"whether their ancestors came over in
the *Mayflower* three centuries ago, or
in the steerage three years ago" . . .

—Calvin Coolidge, at Omaha, October 6, 1925

ACKNOWLEDGMENT

To Clara Louise Leslie, whose researches in the storehouse of Emile Berliner's papers, books and memories paved the way to the construction of this narrative, the author's acknowledgments are here rendered. Her enthusiasm and zeal were incessant sources of helpfulness.   F. W. W.

PREFACE

Mr. Wile's book is one of those wonder stories of perennial fascination, the story of the life of an inventive genius, with its struggles, its devotion and persistence, and its ultimate success. To make this story even more interesting, its hero, still alive and active, has crowned his material success by the capstone of a wise and notable philanthrophy. And he illustrates in his life, as does that great scientist Michael Pupin, the Serbian "immigrant to inventor," in his, the successful taking advantage of America's proverbial opportunity for any youth of brains and industry, from anywhere in the world, to rise to greatness. The German immigrant boy, Emile Berliner, has become one of America's most useful citizens.

But Berliner's contributions to science are not restricted in their beneficence or in their origin to America alone. There are no national boundaries to science. Every nation in the world has contributed to the notable advance of scientific invention, which is the basis of modern civilization. So much is the development of those ideas the handiwork of the men of every nation, that it is almost impossible to assign to any particular nation the whole credit for any one of our great industrial tools or for any one of the great scientific hypotheses by which we conduct so much of our historical life.

Great minds have arisen in every nation who have grasped the work of the past and made it contribute to the progress of the present. These great discoveries, these great inventions, and these great tools which humanity now has at its command have come to us from a thousand sources. They are the cumulated result of constant improvement upon the work of those who have gone before.

The vast populations which the world supports to-day, the high standards of living and comfort with which we are surrounded, are directly due to scientific discovery. It was science that prevented the disaster Malthus predicted as the result of the pressure of the population upon subsistence, for it is science that has increased the productivity of man. A score of men can live in comfort now where only one lived in poverty a hundred years ago.

Discoveries in science are rarely news. There is usually but little about them that is sensational, and they are often intricate and difficult to comprehend. But the public should understand that if we would maintain the continued advance of our material, and to a considerable degree our spiritual life, we must recognize and support scientific research. Such research has great material values, but it also has, and even more importantly, values of high moral and spiritual character. The unfolding of beauty, the aspiration to knowledge, the ever widening penetration into the unknown, the discovery of truth, and, finally, as Huxley says, "the inculcation of veracity of thought," are all of them ample reasons why all good citizens should be interested in the progress of science—and in the careers of men like Emile Berliner.

Herbert Hoover

FOREWORD

From the melting-pot which is the modern United States there has emerged an amalgam which is peculiarly American—an aristocracy of inventive genius. Its members have illumined the progress of mankind for as many years as the Republic has life. Their achievements, indeed, are the milestones which mark America's advance toward her present eminence in the domains of culture, science and the economic arts.

In the veins of American inventors the bloods of many races have been fused. Some of them, like Franklin, Fulton, Morse, Howe, Edison, McCormick, Westinghouse and the Wrights, were products of our own soil, though many were the direct offspring of Transatlantic progenitors. From that same Old-World stock has come to us a contingent of European native-born, which, nurtured in the pioneering atmosphere of the New World, has made rich contributions to the development not only of American civilization, but of the human race. From Scotland came Alexander Graham Bell, inventor of the telephone. Germany sent us Charles Proteus Steinmetz, electrician. From Greek loins sprang another gifted electrician, Nikola Tesla. Hungary bequeathed America a Serbian cattleherd, Michael Idvorsky Pupin, who is to-day a luminary in the firmament of physics and electro-magnetics. To John Ericsson, of Sweden, builder of the *Monitor,* America has just reared a monument on the banks of the Potomac.

A contemporary peer both of many of these American-born and European-born arbiters of the modern universe is the man around whose career of scientific accomplishment and philanthropic zeal this biographical narrative revolves.

It is the story of Emile Berliner, servant of civilization.

It is the story of an immigrant boy who became a man with a billion contacts throughout the world.

It is the story of the telephone, the microphone and the gramophone.

It is the story of one who wrought so wondrously that civilized mankind, defying space, spans continents and oceans by word of mouth.

It is the story of a dreamer whose crude toyings with a soap-box eventuated in a mechanism that enables the President of the United States at will to commune through the air with tens of millions of his fellow-citizens.

It is the story of him who etched the human voice and taught the plowboy to whistle grand opera.

It is the story of a practical idealist who is making child life safer, surer and sweeter.

It is above all the story of the illimitable possibilities of America for the youth in whom the divine spark flickers, no matter how lowly or how alien his origin.

Emile Berliner's story is the story of the microphone, without which neither modern telephony nor its companion in magic, radio broadcasting, would have been possible. It is the story of the indestructible "lateral cut" disk record which brings Caruso and Galli-Curci, and John McCormack and philharmonic orchestras, into the humblest home. It is the story of the movement which led to the general pasteurization of milk through the adoption of government standards.

It is the story of a restlessly active spirit in the endless kingdom of the unexplored, a spirit whom age seems powerless to curb, for, at seventy-five, Emile Berliner is still discovering and inventing. The diamond jubilee of his fruitful life witnessed the addition of "acoustic tiles" to the scroll of his constructive works. His extraordinary vision and unusual aural sense are unimpaired; his physical powers and genial nature, of pristine buoyancy. It would be a rash prophet who would predict that Emile Berliner is an extinct volcano. From that Vesuvius the world is entitled to expect yet other eruptions.

This "Life" is essentially the chronicle of a hero of peace unsung and unheralded. That the story of Emile Berliner is a closed book to the large majority of his fellow-Americans is evidence that self-effacement is not altogether a lost art in our Age of Advertisement.

The year 1926 marks the Fiftieth Anniversary of Bell's invention of the telephone. It is appropriate that the golden jubilee of that boon to human progress should see tardy justice done to the one who contributed effectively to its perfection.

F. W. W.

Washington, D. C.,
July 1, 1926.

CONTENTS

CONTENTS—*Concluded*

APPENDICES

LIST OF ILLUSTRATIONS

LIST OF ILLUSTRATIONS

EMILE BERLINER

EMILE BERLINER

CHAPTER I

BOYHOOD IN GERMANY

INTO that Germany which gave Emile Berliner birth on May 20, 1851, the cult of militarism had come, but not conquered. Men were goose-stepped, but the Mailed Fist was not enthroned. Germany for the most part was what Lord Palmerston called "that damned land of professors."

Liberalism and learning were in the air. The revolution of 1848 had just been waged. The German people were taking to heart the admonition of Fichte, the philosopher, who, in his *Addresses to the Nation* following the Napoleonic humiliation, admonished his countrymen to "replace what they had lost in physical resources by moral strength." The University of Berlin, founded by Fichte, von Humboldt and Schleiermacher in 1813, was in the heyday of its consecrated mission—the inculcation of the doctrine that public education is the true basis of national greatness.

The flower of German industrial might was budding. It was in 1851—the year of Emile Berliner's birth—that Alfred Krupp, an obscure Rhenish steel-maker of Essen, electrified the manufacturing universe by exhibiting at the great Crystal Palace Exhibition in London an ingot of steel weighing two and one-half tons. Germany stood on the threshold of a new birth, destined within a generation to be perverted to the purposes of an insensate imperialism.

In the west of Germany nestled the independent and peaceful little Kingdom of Hanover, pawn of Prussian, French and English dynasties throughout an embattled century. Successively an electorate and a kingdom, and chiefly composed of territories which once belonged to the dukes of Brunswick, Hanover was finally erected into a sovereign realm in 1814, after Waterloo. George V, son of Ernest Augustus, Duke of Cumberland, ascended the throne as King of Hanover during the year in which Emile Berliner was born.

The capital city bore the Kingdom's own name. The Hanover in which Emile first glimpsed the light was a placid community of winding streets, grim castles, quaint buildings, and *Gemüthlichkeit*. It had its court, its garrison, its Anglicized aristocracy, its rather exclusive culture, which included an especially pure type of German speech for which Hanover is famous to this day, and an Institute of Technology that was a center of German engineering progress.

Sir William Herschel, "who pierced the barriers of Heaven" with his telescopes, was a native son of Hanover. Three or four years before Emile Berliner was born there, another *Hannoveraner* came to earth, who was doomed to strike terror to the hearts of men as Berliner was destined to gladden them. His name was Paul von Hindenburg. How vastly different became the chosen paths of these two boys of Hanover, both still alive, and on active service, though septuagenarians! Hindenburg selected the field of Mars as his life avocation and strewed it, before he quit it, baffled and broken, with more of human misery and devastation than war had ever caused before. Berliner was marked for better things. That Divinity which shapes our ends ordained that man-ennobling, not man-killing, works should tax his ingenious energies.

To Samuel Berliner, a small Hanover merchant, and his good wife, Sarah Fridman Berliner, there was born a typically large German family of eleven children. They inhabited a floor of a humble four-story stone building, of which Hanover's bended streets contained many equally inconspicuous. Emile was the fourth child. From his father, a Talmudic scholar of deeply religious fervor, Emile inherited a sense of logic and a respect for biblical teaching. From his mother, a daughter of Cuxhaven, where the Elbe empties into the sea, the boy subconsciously imbibed a wistful longing for the fuller life that beckoned from across the Atlantic,

Through the city of Hanover the River Leine threads its lazy course. On one of its bridges Emile Berliner often would stand in soliloquy, watching the softly rippling current as if crystal-gazing into a beyond he hoped some day to encounter at close range.

The province of Hanover had far too stirring a military history to be devoid of martial pride. The older generation of its menfolk, in Emile Berliner's youth, consisted of those whose fathers had marched with Blücher to overwhelm Napoleon. Theirs were memories and traditions not easily forsaken. One of Emile's school-teachers, a hot-blooded patriot, celebrated his own birthday each year by dispensing with class work and devoting the day to a perfervid glorification of the Battle of Waterloo. "Look at those Hanoverians!" exclaimed Bonaparte, observing their irresistible advance, as the schoolmaster of Hanover depicted it. "You must grow up to be like those soldiers!" the teacher would thunder at his awe-struck class.

For one whole week of every year Hanover gave itself over to the delights and glories of the *Schützenfest* (sharpshooters' festival), a survival of medieval glory. The city donned gala attire. At sunup, before the door of every burgher who was a member of the *Schützenverein*, there would be a rattle of drums to waken him. Soon after dawn Hanover was alive with riflemen, hilariously ready for the great event of each day—a parade to the shooting range in the meadows on the fringe of the city. There all day long and into the night the populace would sing and romp and eat and drink, turning a nominally military affair into what it really was—a merrymaking carnival. At the end of the week, following daily contests in markmanship, the champion sharpshooters was crowned *schützenkönig* (king of sharpshooters), and he remained hero of Hanover till a rival robbed him of his laurels a year later.

King George of Hanover was blind, but insisted upon all the spectacular honors that were his royal prerogative, though he could only hear, and not see, them. He and his Queen were greatly beloved by the Hanoverian people. The road to their *Schloss* was a noble highway along which, for the length of a mile, four giant rows of linden trees separated the thoroughfare into different divisions of travel. On "King's birthday" there was general holiday and a great to-do in Hanover. Shops and houses were gaily illuminated. There was much eating and even more drinking. The troops turned out in gala accouterments. Emile Berliner, like the other youngsters of Hanover, was unfailingly impressed by the gorgeous mounted band, that was uniformed in shining silver armor and led the King's bodyguard of prancing cavalry. Hanover was famed for its fine horses. The pick of its breeds was always preserved for the King's bandsmen and guard. All Hanoverians swelled with pride whenever they told that the six tawny-colored horses that drew Queen Victoria's royal carriage on state occasions in London were Hanover-bred.

The blind King's affliction was a boon to the people, in that it developed in him a great fondness for music, of which the Hanoverians became the beneficiaries. Each year the King contributed a generous sum from his personal fortune so that the citizens of Hanover might enjoy the best music at the Royal Opera for almost next to nothing.

Since time immemorial German towns and cities, even small communities, have prided themselves upon their fine city or state theaters and opera-houses. In the case of *Residenzstadt* (royal capital) like Hanover, these buildings are very beautiful. Emile Berliner's youthful mind was vastly impressed by the architectural splendor of the Hanover *Opernhaus,* and particularly by its gorgeous frescoed curtain depicting the Sun God, Apollo, mounting his chariot for the sunrise.

When Napoleon humbled Prussia after the battle of Jena, he looted the country of many of its choice works of art. Among the things he carted off to the Louvre in Paris was the Hanover opera-house curtain. After Waterloo, the French were despoiled of their ill-gotten gains, and Apollo was restored to his original place in Hanover. There he still hangs.

One of those who availed herself liberally and regularly of the opportunities afforded by the Han-

over royal opera was Sarah Berliner, mother of
Emile. As that child of the Elbe passed on to her
son a longing for life oversea, so she instilled in him
a love for music. Asked to-day to name his boyhood
hobby, Emile Berliner invariably responds: "A
craze for music." It must have been the mainspring
of his inspiration to invent the gramophone. At
boarding school, Emile used to eavesdrop outside
the rooms of wealthier boys who could afford piano
lessons and hum the pieces they practised. A fondness for classical music abides with him.

Hanover pursued the even tenor of its way, a
prosperous province of nearly two million souls,
but as Emile Berliner entered upon his 'teens the
rumble of battle echoed menacingly across the fron-
tier from Prussia. Bismarck was embarking upon
his trilogy of wars that were to unify Germany into
a military empire and launch her upon the aggressive career of a *Weltmacht*. In 1864 Denmark was
assaulted and humbled, and her fair provinces of
Schleswig and Holstein annexed to Prussia. In
1866, Austria was earmarked for attack. King
George of Hanover decided to align his fortunes
with Austria, whereupon the Prussians entered and
occupied Hanover. The Hanoverians fought
bravely, as their forebears did at Waterloo, and de-
feated the Prussians at Langensalza, but two days
later the tide of battle turned against them and
King George's men were compelled to surrender.
That was on June 29, 1866. Three months after-

ward Bismarck annexed Hanover to Prussia over
the futile protest the blind King addressed to
Europe. Thenceforward George V and his house
were exiles on the hospitable soil of Austria.

Emile Berliner had finished a four-year course
at a boarding-chool in Wolfenbüttel, a town about
two hours from Hanover by rail, a year before these
fateful events transpired. The Prussian invasion
photographed itself indelibly upon his young mind.
It recalled itself vividly in 1914 when, in common
with many Americans of German origin, Berliner
was horrified by the invasion of Belgium, though
the Prussians of 1866 had not hacked their way
through Hanover.

Emile was clerking in a dry goods store when the
Uhlans came to his native city. First there were
but three of them, mounted and carrying a flag of
truce. They were the advance guard sent to ask
the burgomaster of Hanover whether there would
be resistance to the Prussian troops standing in
force on the outskirts of the capital. Berliner saw
the Uhlans clattering through the street, each brand-
ishing a pistol, for they evidently feared attack.

Hanover was in no position to defend itself, so
the Uhlans took back word to their commander that
the city could be occupied without danger of a fight.
Then the Prussians poured in. Troops were quar-
tered in the building where Emile worked. It was
a peaceful occupation. But it sowed the seeds of a
hatred that endures in the older generation of Han-

overian breasts to this day. It was not until forty-seven years later, in consequence of one of those strokes of matrimonial statecraft by which kings and queens patch up international differences, that the old house of Hanover, the Cumberlands, consented to have anything to do with the Hohenzollerns. On May 24, 1913, the young Duke Ernest August of Brunswick, "heir to the Hanoverian throne," was married to Princess Victoria Louise of Prussia, only daughter of the haughty German Emperor. There was love-feasting and burying of the hatchet at the Royal Castle of Berlin—the author of this book was present—but the Hanoverians will never forget that it was overbearing Prussia that humiliated and dethroned their beloved blind king and his gracious consort and on September 20, 1866, of painful memory, snuffed out the old kingdom of Hanover and incorporated it within the territory of Prussia. If departed monarchs ever turn in their royal graves for joy, the old blind King of Hanover must have had his moment of vengeful rejoicing when William II, last of the Hohenzollerns, ignominiously fled his throne and his country in the ides of November, 1918.

Emile Berliner was one of thirty-five boy students at the Samsonschule in Wolfenbüttel. He was graduated in 1865 at the age of fourteen and has never been to school since. The grounding he received there, as was the invariable rule in German primary schools, was exceedingly thorough.

He was a good, though not a particularly brilliant pupil. His *Abgangs-Zeugniss* (final report), reveals that he received "excellents" for deportment, industry, application, orderliness and Bible history, but only "very goods," the second highest marks, for history, geography, reading, German, French, singing and gymnastics. Evidently Emile had either small talent for or slight interest in natural history or English, for he scored only "goods" in those branches after four years under *Herr Schuldirektor* Doctor Ehrenberg at Wolfenbüttel.

In two classes young Berliner was highly proficient—drawing and penmanship. He was by far the best draftsman in the Samsonschule. His freehand copies of drawings were almost lithographic. His handwriting is still of the ornate Spencerian type that was considered a great accomplishment in those days. On the occasion of Emile's annual visits to his home in Hanover, during his four years at Wolfenbüttel, he would exhibit with deep pride a set of uncommonly neat copy-books. They are still preserved by him and are proofs of an industrious, if not an illustrious, school career.

Emile Berliner's life as a breadwinner was now upon him. His parents were hard put to it to provide adequately for their extensive brood of youngsters. Emile, it was decided, must shift for himself. He found work as a printer's devil in a job-printing establishment. It required him to be

up and doing winter mornings before daylight and
to break the ice in the basin before he could wash
his face and hands. By seven o'clock, following
a crust and coffee, he had swept out the printery,
and tidied up the type-fonts and hand-presses for
a new day's grind. At nine o'clock he was sent out
to buy the workmen's *zweites Frühstück* (second
breakfast) of beer, cheese and rye bread. Ten
months as a printer's devil without pay except experience were to Emile's credit when he determined
that the printing trade was not to his liking. He
had learned some typesetting, but was tired of working for nothing, and found himself a job as clerk
in a dry-goods store.

Now a lad of sixteen, Berliner's mind for the
first time turned to the inventive. It was the day-
by-day handling of bolts of colored fabric that first
brought it out. He became interested in the methods
by which textiles might be woven. In his free hours
at home he evolved a weaving machine. It was, of
course, not an original idea. But as far as Emile
was concerned, it was an invention. Experts pronounced its principle technically correct and expressed astonishment that an adolescent youth, unaided and without technical equipment, could have
devised so practical a mechanism. They told Samuel and Sarah Berliner that their boy Emile was
ein genialer Kerl—a clever fellow.

Young Berliner plodded on, an industrious, seri-
ous-minded, receptive, observant and rather reticent

youth. German lads did not go in for sports in the 'sixties. Gymnastics represented the first and last word in games. Emile derived his chief pleasure from reading. Night-time, snuggled down into his feather bed beneath a red and black patchwork quilt and by the light of a kerosene lamp, he was accustomed to devour *Robinson Crusoe* and *The Last of the Mohicans*. The wind whipping across the attic roof immediately above him gave frequent reality to the romantic tales which have fired the imaginations of boys in so many lands. Of those two stories of adventure Emile seemed never to tire. He read them dozens of times, and knew whole passages by heart. Probably without his realizing it, Defoe and Fenimore Cooper between them played a subtly vital part, with their classic narratives of self-reliance in new lands, in preparing Emile Berliner for the eventful life about to open up for him in a distant clime.

CHAPTER II

TO THE LAND OF DREAMS

FROM the moment the "Forty-Eighters," the militant Germans of whom Carl Schurz is the most famous, began their great exodus to the United States after the revolution against Prussian autocracy, the eyes of young Germany turned with ever increasing longing toward the New World. Between 1860 and 1870 there poured in from the Fatherland, a stream of immigrants that was limited only by the capacity of steamships to bring them across the Atlantic. Sturdy Germans, whose progenitors were pioneers on American soil along with English, Scottish, Irish and Dutch settlers as long ago as the seventeenth century, leavened our citizenship everywhere.

By 1861 they were already so large in number and so impregnated with American ideals that whole "German regiments" were formed for service in the Union Army during the Civil War. General Franz Sigel commanded a brigade of men who were almost exclusively of Teutonic birth. Carl Schurz was one of Sigel's leaders. Missouri, in the tragic hours of secession, wavered for a while between loyalty to the Union and sympathy with the Confederacy. It was due in no small degree to its numerous German-American element that the great border state was saved for the cause that Abraham Lincoln espoused. Carl Schurz lived in Missouri and afterward represented his state in the United States Senate from 1869 to 1875.

Thoughts and dreams of America—*das Land der unbegrenzten Möglichkeiten* (the land of unlimited possibilities), as it came to be called in more modern times—now were flitting through Emile Berliner's head. Like all young Hanoverians, he loathed Prussian militarism, under whose boot-heel the independence of his native land lay crushed. Denmark had been bullied, beaten and despoiled of her fairest provinces. Imperial Austria, as the price of annihilating defeat at Königgrätz, was cowed into the ignominy of a Prussian vassal. The German Confederation having been annulled, the North German Confederation had been set up under the spurred and helmeted supremacy of Prussia. Hanover, Hesse-Cassel, Nassau, Frankfort and other provinces were deprived of their sovereignty and herded like sheep into the Prussian realm. Bismarck ruled at Berlin, drunk with power and successive triumphs in the fields of war and statecraft. Such was the depressing vision that loomed before the eyes of upgrowing Germans in the years of Emile Berliner's budding manhood. It was not a vista to stir the imagination of a lad in whom the

BERLINER'S PLAYGROUND WHEN A BOY IN HANOVER

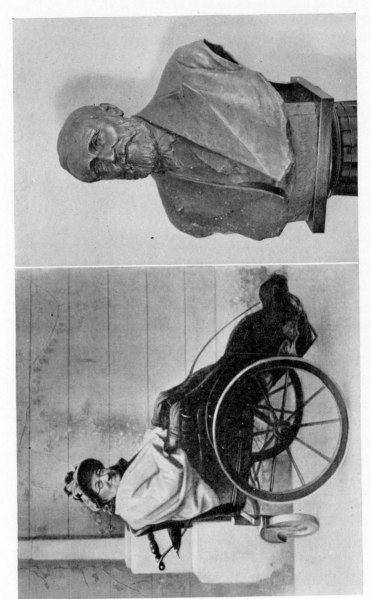

MR. BERLINER'S MOTHER AND FATHER

fires of constructive achievement were, subconsciously, aglow and so soon to be kindled into a flame.

The alumnus of Wolfenbüttel, now in his nineteenth year and eking out a drab existence as a dry-goods clerk, first had his day-dreaming turned concretely toward the Golden West by the return to Hanover of an old family friend. Nathan Gotthelf had emigrated to the United States many years before and was now a small, though prosperous, merchant in Washington, D. C. Gotthelf came back to Germany in 1869, to visit his native haunts and spread the gospel of the El Dorado that awaited exploration and conquest everywhere in "free America."

His story fascinated Emile Berliner. The youth determined that if parental consent could be obtained, he would cross the Atlantic at the earliest possible moment. It was not long afterward that in one of the humble homes of Hanover a group of wide-eyed youths, consumed with envy of the good fortune about to overtake their most enterprising comrade, gathered around a table laden all over its checkered cloth with potato-pancakes, rye bread, Swiss cheese and beer. In the midst of his companions sat Emile Berliner, hero of the occasion. It was an *Abschiedsfeier* (farewell party) in his honor. He was about to take the long, long leap and seek his fortune overseas.

Nathan Gotthelf promised to give Emile work in

the little dry-goods store on Seventh Street, Washington, immediately upon the lad's arrival in America. It would be a modest beginning, but it was an assured one, and amid friends. The Berliner family council had consented, and now Emile was to join the adventuring throng that was turning its back on militarized Germany. It would be an instructive thing if some day it could be ascertained, in measurable terms, what nineteenth-century Germany might have become if so many of her intrepid young spirits had not been driven away by the depressing influence of the Prussian goose-step.

Emile Berliner was of military age when he elected to become an *Amerikaner*. Bismarck, Moltke, Roon and the puppet King of Prussia, soon to be the self-consecrated Kaiser Wilhelm "the Great," were busily making their battle toilet for Prussia's next war of conquest—the contest with France. Young Berliner had passed with flying colors the examination for the *Einjährige-Freiwillige* (one-year volunteer) term in the Prussian Army. Under this system, in vogue until the outbreak of the World War, a young German was absolved from the onerous obligations of three, later two, consecutive years of service in barracks during early manhood. All lads of adequate mental equipment and of even moderately well-to-do family took the *Einjährige-Freiwillige* examination. It was a certificate of exceptional culture.

Although the authorities were keeping minute

tab on every ounce of Prussian military resources, for the war with France was to break forth in all its fury within a few months, April 27, 1870, found Emile Berliner unmolestedly preparing to shake the dust of Germany from his feet. He was now on the threshold of his nineteenth birthday. It was a tearful farewell he took of his parents, brothers, sisters and cronies. His father he was never to see again. Upon his head the devoted mother, Sarah Berliner, laid a hand that betokened unuttered prayers for Emile's spiritual salvation and material welfare in the land of his impending adoption. The lad's heart was heavier than he cared to show before kith and kin. He was face to face with an incalculable future. Emotion subdued all inclination to elation, though inwardly Emile thirsted for the new experiences that were beckoning to him in the great republic across three thousand miles of salt water.

A depressing mist was falling as Emile stepped, baggage laden, from the old-fashioned train that brought him from Hanover to Hamburg. The famous Elbe port had not become the mighty world harbor into which the genius of Albert Ballin was destined to convert it, but the argosies of the Hamburg-Amerikanische Paketfahrt-Aktien-Gesellschaft already traversed the seven seas, and from the same far-flung waters came to Hamburg the ships of all the nations. "My Field is the World" has been the "Hapag's" official motto since the Hamburg-American line's foundation. That might have been the

slogan on Emile's coat-of-arms, too, had the Ber-
liners boasted a family crest, for the intrepid young
Hanoverian who was setting out for new land that
day in April, 1870, was himself destined to girdle
the globe, though in other ways than Hamburg's
ships.

Emile, who had never seen ocean ships or
sniffed the air of the sea, was deeply impressed
by the forest of masts that always dominates the
perspective in Hamburg. He speedily found his
bearings. He was electrified by the consciousness
that with every step America was growing nearer.
The realization made his crude baggage seem lighter
as he trudged for endless cobblestoned blocks har-
borward and to the water's edge.

At the Hamburg-American line wharves an immense hustle and bustle raged. Great hulks of
longshoremen, men reared to the hardy trade of the
sea—Germans, Frisians, Helgolanders, Dutchmen,
Danes, Swedes, Norwegians—worked like beavers
loading and unloading cargo from vessels moored
to the docks in a line longer than the eye could follow. Wharves were not of steel and concrete in
those days, and through the gaping cracks of the
unhewn floors of the docks where he was now
arrived, Emile could see and hear the water of the
Elbe splashing and swishing against the piles, and
feel those timber pinions swaying now and then as
the water gurgled in with a bit of a surge. The
whole scene filled the Hanoverian emigrant boy,

land-lubber as he was, with a solemn wonder. But it was athrob with life—the life into which he felt he was about to plunge—so wonder melted speedily into enthusiasm, and he became conscious of a leaping anxiety to clamber aboard his ship of destiny.

There she was, tied to the dock, far down the row of barges and cargo boats crunching at the pier, and standing forth a queen among her ignobler sister craft, for she was the *Hammonia* and bore the proud name of the patron goddess of the Free Hanseatic City of Hamburg. From her black and red smokestack smoke floated lazily, indicating that the *Hammonia's* furnaces were alight and her boilers ready to propel her on still another transatlantic journey.

The *Hammonia* glowed before Emile Berliner's enraptured gaze the embodiment of all his boyhood dreams of a great ship. Brass rails agleam—spotless cleanliness—ship-shapeness all about. The *Hammonia* was not the liner *de luxe* of this ostentatious age. But she was a *Leviathan* of her time, and, of course, in Emile's eyes, a miracle ship. He mounted the gangplank that led into the second cabin, and Germany was bereft of a genius.

CHAPTER III

THE MAKING OF AN AMERICAN

OCEAN greyhounds in the 'seventies had only the speed of bulldogs, and needed just as much tenacity. They plowed the Atlantic between Hamburg and New York laboriously in weeks, not days, and the *Hammonia,* with Emile Berliner aboard, required for her voyage exactly a fortnight. It was a stormy crossing. Second-cabin accommodations fifty-five years ago were inferior to steerage facilities to-day. Humble as were Emile's home comforts, he missed them sadly.

He and his shipmates had everything in common. Like himself, they were about to become prospectors in the gold-fields of Opportunity. Their days and nights aboard ship were weird and wonderful hours of speculation and anticipation. Some of the *Hammonia's* emigrant cargo were more fortunate than young Berliner. They had flesh and blood awaiting them in America, and homes into which the new arrivals would be welcomed, literally, as brothers, sisters, sons or daughters. Parents were aboard, too, bound for loving firesides established by pioneering and subsequently fortunate offspring in American town or country. Emile's lot was to be cast among friends. But beyond that lay a vacuum. He was of stout heart. The answer to a question once leveled at him by this chronicler is significant. "What was your chief emotion as a poor German boy about to be put down, a complete stranger, on United States soil?" Quoth Berliner: "Anxiety to know how long it would take me to become a thorough American!"

The Goddess of Liberty was not enlightening the world in the days when the *Hammonia* slipped into New York harbor. Nor was there that ultra-modern institution, the immigration quota. America in those halcyon times welcomed to her capacious bosom the oppressed, the ambitious, the liberty-loving of all climes, regardless of whether they were Nordics, Latins or Orientals. Our industries were not even infant industries; they were little more than in the conception stage. The illimitable wealth of our mines and agricultural fields had not been scratched. Railroads were in the chrysalis phase. The clamor was for unskilled labor to hasten the colossal economic development on the verge of which the giant republic trembled. Europe was the bottomless well from which the United States proceeded eagerly to draw its human supplies. On they came—in torrents—in the 'seventies, and the 'eighties, and the 'nineties, and in the early decades of the new century, till we became a satiated, and, as some of our detractors aver, a selfish, folk, barring our gates and proclaiming that America was no longer an asylum. *Tempora mutantur, nos et mutamur in illis.* . . .

Apollo, the Sun God, whose allegorical splendor as reflected on the great Hanover opera-house curtain is one of Emile's indelible memories, was holding watch and ward over him, for the Jersey coast was bathed in golden sunshine as Berliner's ship docked at Hoboken. The young emigrant's English vocabulary was primitive, and he was happy to be met by a New York acquaintance of his Washington benefactor. Unfamiliarity with a strange country's language is an appalling and a depressing thing. He who is responsible for this record endured that experience in Berliner's native land of Germany, though under immensely less disadvantageous conditions than those Emile now faced. Men yearn at such times for Volapuk or some other universal medium more effective than the sign language.

Emile was awed by the bigness of New York, although there were no Woolworth Towers then, nor Brooklyn bridges, nor subways, nor even cable cars. The horse was still king. Ferry-boats are the only survivors of the Gotham that Berliner first knew—Edith Wharton's *Age of Innocence*. He expressed a desire to reach Washington as soon as possible. So, after half a day of itinerant sight-seeing, he was put on the train for the capital, as green as the Jersey, Pennsylvania and Delaware grass he was soon to inspect from his first American car-window. To Washington, the telegraph carried the following terse warning of an impending event:

> New York, May 11, 1870
> Messrs. Gotthelf, Behrend and Co.,
> 818 Seventh Street,
> Washington, D. C.
> Berliner will start most likely to-night or to-morrow morning.
> Jacob Davidson

Berliner has lived to put so much of sunshine into the dark places of the world that one is often constrained to think his inspiration came from the weather conditions that first greeted him here. His most vivid impressions of early hours and days in America are recollections of super-abundant sunshine. He had come out of North Germany, which has its moments of sunshine, but its sieges of gray, damp, bleak and cheerless atmosphere. In his first letter to his parents—foreign postage in 1870 was forty cents the half ounce—Emile mentioned the constant sunlight as one of America's principal characteristics. No doubt it lifted up his soul in his occasional spells of homesickness or other depression. He thought it accounted for the omnipresent optimism in the American nature.

It was to the sordid Washington of reconstruction days that Emile Berliner came on May 12, 1870. The first presidency of General Ulysses S. Grant was in its tempestuous midst. It was the era of the carpetbaggers. The South, still bleeding and sullen, failed to find in Grant, the president, the generous conqueror who declined Lee's sword at Appomattox. "At Appomattox," says David Saville Muzzey, history mentor of so many thousands of American schoolboys, "Grant had been noble. Yet as President he upheld the disgraceful negro governments of the Reconstruction Act, and constantly furnished troops to keep the carpetbag and scalawag officials in power in the South, in order to provide Republican votes for congressmen and presidential electors."

Not only were Reconstruction methods keeping open the Civil War wounds of the South, but political corruption everywhere was rife. Muzzey teaches that

"Probably the tone of public morality was never so low in all of our country's history, before or since, as it was in the years of Grant's Administration (1869-1877), although a more honest President never sat in the White House. Large contracts for supplies of food, clothing, ammunition and equipment had to be filled on short notice. Men grew rich on fraudulent deeds. Our state legislatures and municipal governments fell into the hands of corrupt 'rings.' Corruption reached the highest offices of state. Grant's secretary of war, William W. Belknap, resigned in order to escape impeachment for sharing the graft from the dishonest management of army posts in the West. The President's private secretary, Babcock, was implicated in frauds which robbed the government of its revenue tax on whisky. Western stage-coach lines, in league with corrupt post-office officials, made false returns of the amount of business done along their routes, and secured large appropriations from Congress for carrying the mails. Members of Congress so far lost their sense of official propriety as to accept large amounts of railroad stock as 'presents' from men who wanted legislative favors for their roads.''

That was the America which Emile Berliner was first to know. It is probably a blessing that neither his knowledge of the English language nor his predilections permitted him to become contaminated by the atmosphere in which he found himself at Washington, else it might have turned the young German idealist in disgust from the America which had tempted him away from native heath.

Emile set diligently about the task he considered to be paramount—to make himself "a good American" with the least possible delay. The conquest of our language became his first objective. He listened to it intently in the Gotthelf store. He read Hawthorne and Longfellow. He studied the *Quarterly Reviews* of England in the old Y. M. C. A. reading-rooms at Ninth and D Streets, not far from his place of work in Washington. His literary bent was in the direction of the serious. He worshiped indiscriminately in churches of all denominations, in order to hear eloquent sermons and accustom his ear to good English. At his place of employment some of the wrapping-paper consisted of surplus copies of the *Congressional Record,* then printed and sold by a private firm. Statesmen in the Reconstruction era were as loquacious as they are to-day. The *Congressional Record* was correspondingly bulky. Emile took copies regularly to his lodgings and from them imbibed a familiarity with the oratorical style of those florid days.

Having lived to see Washington "the city of magnificent distances," and having himself become one of its important property-owners, Emile Berliner is fond of comparing the national capital of to-day with the Washington of the Grant era. Then it was an overgrown, unkempt community of sixty thousand, giving small promise of conversion into the splendid world metropolis which, despite the continuing excrescence of Pennsylvania Avenue, it is to-day. When John Hay came to Washington as an assistant private secretary to President Lincoln, he wrote:

"Warsaw (Illinois) dull? It shines before my eyes like a social paradise compared with this miserable sprawling village, which imagines itself a city because it is wicked, as a boy thinks he is a man when he smokes and swears. I wish I could by wishing find myself in Warsaw."

Berliner's early Washington was a town of horse-cars as the sole means of public transportation. The gorgeous barouche and pair was the limousine of the day. Colored coachmen and footmen were the quintessence of elegance. Gas was the most luxurious form of illumination, and farmers coming to city hotels occasionally blew it out and were asphyxiated. Washington had no sewage or filtration of water. At meals Potomac River water was served in china pitchers so that those about to reduce the invisible supply of microbes might not be able to detect their presence in the muddy yellow fluid. The city was full of typhoid and malaria. There were no shade trees, such as now make the great avenues of the capital uniquely lovely, except in the grounds of the Smithsonian Institution and the Soldiers' Home. To both of those parks people would flee for relief from the heat of the equatorial climate of the District of Columbia. Rock Creek Park did not yet exist, except as a wilderness.

Gaunt telegraph poles, from which wires interlaced the streets in all directions, accentuated the city's crude exterior. Italian organ-grinders, with their dancing monkeys, were popular attractions. Their canned music consisted mostly of Civil War songs like *Marching Through Georgia* and *Captain Jinks,* for the martial spirit was still abroad through Washington and the North. As fervently was *Dixie* sung and played throughout the seemingly irreconcilable South.

President Grant, short, stocky and democratic, was a familiar figure on Pennsylvania Avenue in the afternoons, as he took his constitutional, hands clasped behind his back, unfailingly accompanied by his cigar, and minus guards of any kind. Through the windows of the swagger hotels of the capital, now ramshackle survivors of their ancient glory,

lazy politicians in whiskers and wide-brimmed hats
stretched their legs by the hour, as they discussed
the state of the Union amid contests in long-distance
tobacco-spitting across the littered sidewalks of
"the Avenue."

Now and then cattle would be driven through or
across that dilapidated boulevard of state. On the
southern side of the nation's Via Triumphalis
coursed a murky canal along which scows were
tediously towed. Emile Berliner thought of Hanover
and other well-kept cities in Germany, with their
civic pride and cleanliness and love of architectural
beauty, and found it difficult to reconcile the cobble-
stones, brick pavements and general primitiveness
of Washington with his preconception of the capital
of great America.

The Americanization of Emile Berliner set in
with a change in the spelling of his given name. At
birth he was christened "Emil," but he had been in
Washington only a few weeks when he decided to
refurbish it into "Emile," adding the final "e" as
an Anglo-Saxon touch. He thought it would materially fortify his morale in the de-Prussianizing
process in which he now was sturdily immersed.
Berliner has always been zealously watchful that
nobody, particularly since the World War, in addressing him or referring to him in print, shall
forget that the spelling of his name is the Anglo-
Saxon Emile, and not the German Emil. One of the
considerations that impelled him to make the change

was the marked contrast he found in America in the treatment of young men. Here, he soon discovered, they were treated as equals. In Prussia-Germany, elders and superiors looked down upon them in a spirit of military hauteur.

To our whimsical national habits, weird and strange to the newcomer, Berliner steadily adjusted himself in Washington. An Italian street-corner vender taught him how to eat peanuts and bananas—arts then unknown to a German boy. Ice-cream soda became another early accomplishment, thanks to the ministrations of a friendly druggist who mixed his own sirups and produced concoctions that passed comprehension. Emile became especially fond of a mixture of coffee-sirup and chocolate, which he himself designed in a spirit of bibulous adventure. It eventually became popular with many patrons of the drug-store as "half-and-half." Berliner calls it one of his first inventions.

Three years had passed, and Emile Berliner, now at man's estate, began to think of his future. He had no definite plans regarding it. His time in the United States thus far had been assiduously devoted to the earning of his living, the learning of English and the absorption of American ideas. In all three of those directions he made substantial progress, except with regard to a livelihood. That he had earned, and little more. He found time to take up the study of music. Now and then he thought music might become his profession. He knew such a life would delight the mother he had left behind in Hanover. Emile took some lessons in both piano and violin, and still plays both of those instruments. But he played by ear only. It is his strange sort of eyesight that kept him from becoming a sight reader of music. "I have an unusual kind of vision," he explains. "If my attention is called to one person in a group of people, I see no one else in the group. This is the reason I never went further in music. I couldn't see notes ahead *in groups*."

Berliner's gray brown eyes are almost piercing—not intimidating in their effect, as such eyes often are, but kindly, and endowed with an intense power of concentration. To-day, at seventy-five, before Berliner begins to read, he takes off his glasses. He appears to wear them principally for decorative effect. They are nose-glasses and dangle most of the time from the black cord which anchors them to his person. He suffers from slight near-sightedness, but has not needed a change of lenses for twenty-five years. For close work, his eyes still serve him better unaided. They seem to have been given him to look keenly and fruitfully into the future.

CHAPTER IV

A ROLLING STONE

EMILE BERLINER had lived in the United States long enough at the end of three years to imbibe the American spirit of adventure. He had conquered our language; absorbed the habits of young men of his age, including a predilection to better himself; and longed for fields of conquest other than the drab District of Columbia. National activities, in a financial and mercantile sense, were centered in New York City almost exclusively. To achieve fame and fortune in the metropolis was the goal of every ambitious American youth. They were the times that fired Horatio A. Alger with inspiration for the Oliver Optic stories—when virtue in Broadway was still its own reward.

The year in which Berliner decided to pull up stakes in Washington and tempt fate in New York was a period of unparalleled crash and smash in business America. A fainter heart than that which beat beneath the bosom of the young Hanoverian would have preferred the dull certainty of life along the Potomac to the atmosphere of devastation and depression which prevailed on the Hudson.

31

Between 1869 and 1873 railroad building proceeded at a feverish rate in the United States. Some
twenty-four thousand miles of lines, or more than
three times as many as were built during the preceding four years, were constructed. Business was
at the high tide of prosperity. But in its wake there
ensued an orgy of wild speculation, wide-spread extension of credit and inflated values. The bubble
burst with tragic and annihilating suddenness. The
great banking house of Jay Cooke went to the wall—
an event as transcendent as would to-day be the
failure of J. P. Morgan and Company, or the National City Bank, if so catastrophic a thing can be
imagined. Cooke's institution had been of priceless
service in floating Union Government loans during
the Civil War. Without the bank's aid, Lincoln and
Grant could hardly have carried on.

Every money center in the land felt the shock of
the Cooke collapse. Lesser houses, caught in the
eddies of mistrust and fear which boiled up in all
directions, went under by the dozen. Many people
held Congress responsible for releasing the economic furies because of the passage of a currency bill,
known as "the Crime of 'Seventy-Three," because
of its discrimination against the silver dollar.
Therefore both gold and silver were freely coined
on terms of parity. Either precious metal was ex-
changeable at the Treasury for an equivalent weight
in coin. That is to say, a citizen could obtain gold
coins for his silver or silver coins for his gold at the

rate of sixteen ounces of silver to one ounce of gold. Such was the parity that William Jennings Bryan converted into a popular political slogan in 1896, when he sought the presidency on a "free silver" platform. Bryan demanded that the "Crime of 'Seventy-Three" should be expiated by re-legalizing "the free and unlimited coinage of silver" at the ratio of sixteen to one. "You shall not crucify mankind upon a cross of gold," he shrieked in his immortal peroration at the Democratic national convention in Chicago. Bryan was overwhelmed at the succeeding election mainly because the country feared a repetition of the crisis of 1873.

As always happens on these cyclonic occasions—panics in the United States, before creation of the Federal Reserve system, recurred with regularity about every twenty years—the panic of 1873 cleared the economic atmosphere. Sturdy oaks of commerce and finance were brought down before the storm spent its fury. Families which had never known anything but affluence were reduced to poverty overnight. Historic "Black Friday" saw the panic raging at the zenith of its destructive force. Thenceforward the stabilizing process set steadily in, but the back-wash of the incidental tidal wave of bankruptcy spread its ruinous effects over many years.

The panic of 1873 was one of the things known in Emile Berliner's native country by the expressive idiom of *Kinderkrankheiten*—the diseases of childhood. America was in its economic childhood—

undergoing its growing pains. Wall Street lived to
learn that the great upheaval was one of the most
salutary events in financial America's hectic history.
Two men emerged from the encircling gloom as
heroes and victors—Jay Gould and "Jim" Fisk,
who operated together as speculators on the right
side of the tempestuous market, especially in railroad "deals."

In the business rack and ruin amid which Emile
Berliner arrived at New York for the second time
within three years, he was aware that he could not
be a chooser, though he was hardly a beggar, for he
had saved some of his meager wages as a dry-goods
clerk in Washington. He speedily realized that he
would have to take the work he could get without
waiting for the kind he preferred. It is interesting
to note that, though now aged twenty-two, Berliner
had as yet no concrete notions whatever as to his
future. His anxieties were concerned exclusively
with the bread and butter question. He had not been
educated for a profession or any special vocation.
His equipment consisted entirely of a studious nature, zest for hard work, ambition, natural intelligence and ample self-confidence. Despite a distinct
trace of intuitiveness in his make-up, the inventive
streak in him had not yet shone.

Berliner was interested, but not engrossed, in
scientific achievement, and, of course, had had no
sort of preparation for it. So he turned in New
York to the first employment that came to hand. It

was of variegated hue. He sold glue. He painted
the backgrounds of enlarged tin-type portraits—his
talent for drawing stood him in stead for that
artistry. He gave German lessons. The United
States was still awed by the results of the Franco-
Prussian war and Bismarck's creation of the
German Empire by blood and iron. Americans
acquired a correspondingly new interest in the
Fatherland. There was a bull market for instruction in the language which Mark Twain described as
"the only one in the world in which you can travel
all day in one sentence without changing cars."

New York having failed to launch Berliner on
the tide that leads to fortune, the spirit moved him
to harken to the advice of Horace Greeley: "Young
man, go west!" In literal truth, it was not Greeley's admonition so much as an advertisement in a
New York newspaper that turned Berliner's
thoughts in the direction of the setting sun. "Milwaukee gents' furnishing house wants enterprising
young man to go on the road" was the seductive
legend that attracted Berliner's attention and as
promptly determined him to don the armor of a
knight of the gripsack and sample-case.

Commercial travelers were already known as
"drummers." They were the real ambassadors of
trade. Advertising, as we know it to-day, was non-
existent. The mail-order house was as undiscovered
a phenomenon as the automobile. "Drummers"
made good wages and were regarded indispensable

members of business society. Berliner applied for
the Milwaukee job and got it. Behind the counter at
Gotthelf, Behrend and Company's store in Washington he had learned the mysteries of collars and
cuffs, neckties and suspenders, and the other habili-
ments of haberdashery. When he turned up in
Milwaukee, then almost as German a city as his native Hanover itself, his employers-to-be were agree-
ably surprised by his familiarity with the language
of the ''gents' furnishings'' tribe.

Wisconsin provided young Berliner with many
reminders of the Fatherland besides its omnipresent
German population. In the first place, it was bleak
and cold—Berliner arrived from the East in a temperature of thirty-three degrees below zero and with
a pair of frozen ears. The Dairy State flowed with
milk and cheese, as well as lager beer, and those
institutions helped to keep Berliner from growing
homesick, too. His employers told him he was to
travel up and down the Mississippi River between
St. Paul and St. Louis, and out to the Missouri
River as far west as Omaha. The western spaces
were even more ''open'' than they are to-day.
Distances between settled communities were greater
and conditions immeasurably more primitive. The
''trade'' Berliner was assigned to canvass was of a
sort to test every ounce of salesmanship in his green
make-up. For the most part it consisted of
David Harums who had gone west to grow up with
the country and could bargain the bark off a tree.

Travel was principally by Mississippi River barges—tedious, hot, uncomfortable and slow. Berliner had to learn to speak a wholly different brand of American language than that he acquired on the Atlantic seaboard. He found himself in the presence of the mid-western drawl, and, as his wanderings took him down river, he had to master the lingo of the Mississippi darky, who spoke a dulcet tongue that was all his own. Many of the rural storekeepers to whom Berliner offered Milwaukee creations in "gents' " finery were Mark Twain's people—the droll, shrewd types among whom Huckleberry Finn and Tom Sawyer grew up. The young drummer, with his microscopic mind, found lively amusement in studying the Main Street types of the era.

Berliner was a satisfactory, if not a scintillating, traveling salesman, but he did not succumb to the lure of the Middle West. After considerably less than a year's dabbling in "gents' furnishings" he retraced his steps to the East. For the third time he arrived in New York with life stretching before him a complete blank. Yet the rolling stone unwittingly now was heading for the path along which he was to reach a worthy destination.

The year 1875 was tapering to its end when Berliner obtained work in the laboratory of Doctor Constantine Fahlberg, an analyst of sugar by occupation. While Fahlberg was respected in the limited community which had need of his professional services, he was not looked upon as the scientific genius he later was recognized to be. It was several years afterward that Fahlberg discovered saccharin, the intensely sweet crystalline substance derived from coal tar and now in so common use in both industry and medicine.

In one of Emile Berliner's scrap-books is a clipping dated 1886, which contains Fahlberg's own story of the discovery of saccharin.

It reads:

"One evening I was so interested in my laboratory that I forgot about supper until quite late, and then rushed off for a meal without stopping to wash my hands. I sat down, broke a piece of bread, and put it to my lips. It tasted unspeakably sweet. I did not ask why it was so, probably because I thought it was some cake or sweetmeat. I rinsed my mouth with water and dried my mustache with my napkin, when, to my surprise, the napkin tasted sweeter than the bread. Then I was puzzled. I again raised my goblet, and, as fortune would have it, applied my mouth where my fingers had touched it before. The water seemed sirup. It flashed upon me that I was the cause of the singular universal sweetness. I accordingly tasted the end of my thumb, and found that it surpassed any confectionery I had ever eaten. I saw the whole thing at a glance. I had discovered or made some coal tar substance which out-sugared sugar."

Fahlberg's discovery of saccharin gave him fame. Berliner remained at the laboratory in the humble and unromantic capacity of a general handy man and bottle-washer. But he did improve his opportunities at Fahlberg's workshop to the point of

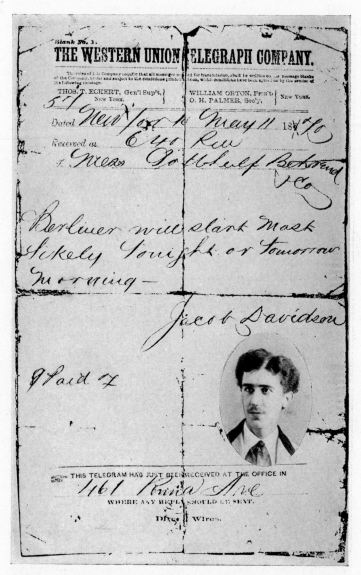

TELEGRAM SENT ON EMILE BERLINER'S ARRIVAL IN THE UNITED
STATES IN 1870. INSET, MR. BERLINER IN 1872

STORE IN WASHINGTON WHERE MR. BERLINER CLERKED

learning to analyze raw sugar. The knowledge whetted his interest in research.

Many of his evenings Berliner now spent at Cooper Institute, that meritorious university of the New York poor for the past three generations. He was a regular habitué of its library and indulged his growing fondness for scientific books and publications. It was while frequenting Cooper Institute that Berliner struck up an acquaintance with a man who, as the result of a trifling episode, was destined to play an important part in the shaping of Berliner's career. Around the corner from his boarding-house was a drugstore into which Berliner often dropped for a chat with the proprietor, August Engel. The druggist took a fancy to his visitor and a whimsical interest in the young fellow's ambitions to develop his scientific bent. One evening, as the pair was standing around the coal-stove which, from the center of the store, radiated heat throughout the premises, they drifted into a casual discussion of the laws of physics. Berliner had a smattering of the subject from his readings at Cooper Institute.

"I've got a book on physics that I'll give you," the druggist said. It was forthwith produced and eagerly accepted. Berliner still has it. It is a German book, published in 1854 and entitled *Synopsis of Physics and Meteorology*. The author was Doctor Johann Mueller, professor at the University of Freiburg-in-Breisgau. The book was replete with wood engravings and in its day was a classic work.

In Mueller's work were two chapters which enlisted Emile Berliner's particular interest. They
dealt, respectively, with acoustics and electricity.
Electricity was then a very limited branch of science, but Mueller treated it with great clarity and
intelligence. The book contains an illustrated story
showing how Luigi Galvani, the eighteenth-century
professor of anatomy at Bologna, discovered fluid
electricity through a frog's leg which he had hung
on a copper wire to dry. As everybody knows, gal-
vanometers, galvanoplastics and all the other
terminology connected with the "galvanic" branch
of physics get their names from the Italian scientist.
Synopsis of Physics and Meteorology forthwith became Emile Berliner's faithful guide, philosophic
text-book and scientific friend. He had his nose in
it day and night. It set him to dreaming and thinking. He studied it till he knew his favorite chapters
almost by heart.

Berliner now had quit his bottle-washing job at
Fahlberg's laboratory and climbed several rungs up
the economic ladder by becoming a bookkeeper in a
feed store at twelve dollars a week.

One evening after work, while boarding a street-
car on his way home to supper, Berliner encountered a friendly face. It was that of B. J. Behrend,
now proprietor of the dry-goods store in Washington, where Berliner had his first job three years
before. Forthwith ensued an orgy of reminiscence
over the old days. There was a new and different

Washington, Berliner was told, and a city much richer in opportunity than the crude capital of Reconstruction days—so ran the seductive tale of the long-lost friend, who gave persuasive assurance of a future on the Potomac for a fellow as worldly wise as Emile Berliner had become.

Berliner listened to the siren song, and arranged to return to Washington (it was the end of 1876) to resume his clerking job in the Seventh Street store. Before he left New York he took out his first naturalization papers. Come what may, he was determined to work out his salvation as an American citizen. America was on the brink of an era of stupendous invention. In its development the youth of Hanover was ordained to play a rôle he wot not of.

CHAPTER V

THE year 1876 marked far more than the one hundredth anniversary of the birth of the nation. It ushered in a new industrial age. We remember 1876 as the period of the great Centennial at Philadelphia—as the patriotic celebration of a century of American independence under the sovereign Stars and Stripes. But the year more richly deserves to be indexed in national history as the advent of a renaissance. It launched American inventive ingenuity upon a cycle of achievement that was to reconstruct the activities of the human race and turn them into channels beyond all imaginings.

It can not be said that invention in America was a lost art during the first hundred years of our liberation from the British yoke. The inventive spirit of the "founding fathers" and of their generations of hardy offspring was far from being either extinct or in decay. Franklin's lightning rod, Fulton's steamboat, Whitney's cotton gin, Morse's electric telegraph, Goodyear's vulcanized rubber, Howe's sewing machine, Ericsson's *Monitor,* Westinghouse's air brake, and Sholes' typewriter were all discov-

42

ered or devised prior to 1876. But brilliant in conception and important in results as were those master strokes of American genius, the age which the Centennial introduced was to be distinguished by discoveries of even more transcendent importance.

In their effects upon the lives and times of men, the ideas about to spring from American brains were ordained to be revolutionary. The nation and the world were at the threshold of the telephone, the talking machine, the incandescent lamp, the arc light, the gasoline motor, the trolley car, the self-binder, the skyscraper, the automobile, the motion picture, high speed steel and the airplane. Spoiled moderns, who look upon all these boons to existence as matters of course, can not easily comprehend the state of relative primitiveness which prevailed in the United States at the time of the Centennial. Radio, that quintessential accompaniment of present-day life, was not remotely dreamed of when the Liberty Bell broadcast a new century of American freedom on the Fourth of July, 1876. The Centennial was the birthday of an epoch.

Men, women and children seemed to scent the dawn of the new era. There was stimulus in the very atmosphere America breathed. Inspired by its colossal achievements thus far in wringing an empire from out of the primeval soil, the young giant of the western world stretched its sturdy muscles and expanded its mighty chest in proud consciousness of latent strength. It resolved upon fresh conquests in the fields of material progress and upon consistent development along the paths of enlightened democracy. Such was the spirit of 1876.

No one was more fervently inoculated with it than Emile Berliner. He, like nearly every young man of ambition in the United States, had had a look at the Centennial, though only a cursory one, for it was confined to a day's holiday trip from New York. Music filled his soul at the time more than electromagnetics. He did not know, when he visited Philadelphia, that Alexander Graham Bell's telephone— such as it was—was modestly on exhibit at the Centennial. When asked not long ago for the outstanding impression of his visit to the great international exposition in Fairmount Park, Berliner said: "My recollection of seeing Offenbach conduct the Centennial orchestra!" Yet the Centennial spirit was destined to leave an indelible impress upon Berliner's life. Another Emil—Rathenau, founder of the famous Allgemeine Electricitäts Gesellschaft (General Electric Company) of Berlin— came away from Philadelphia, declaring that the Centennial "had electrified his soul." Eventually Rathenau electrified the Fatherland in a literal sense by superintending the first telephone exchange in Germany and organizing the greatest electrical manufacturing concern in Europe.

The spirit of 1876 was graphically depicted by Emile Berliner twelve years after the Centennial when, speaking within a stone's throw of Independence Hall, he addressed the Franklin Institute of Philadelphia. On May 16, 1888, at the first public demonstration of the gramophone, he referred in these terms to the Centennial cycle:

"The last year in the first century of the history of the United States was a remarkable one in the history of science.

"There appeared about that period something in the drift of scientific discussions which, even to the mind of an observant amateur, foretold the coming of important events.

"The dispute of Religion *versus* Science was once more at its height; prominent daily papers commenced to publish weekly discussions on scientific topics; series of scientific books, in attractive popular form, were eagerly bought by the cultured classes; popular lectures on scientific subjects were sure of commanding enthusiastic audiences; the great works on evolution had just begun to take root outside of the small circle of logical minds from which they had emanated and which had fostered them; scientific periodicals were expectantly scanned for new information; and the minds of both professionals and amateurs were on the *qui vive*.

"Add to this the general excitement prevailing on account of the forthcoming Centennial celebration with its crowning event, so dear to this nation of inventors, the world's exhibition, and even those who did not at the time experience the effects of an atmosphere pregnant with scientific ozone can, in their minds, conjure up the pulsating, swaying and turbulent sea of scientific research of that period. Science evidently was in labor.

"The year 1876 came, and when the jubilee was at its very height, and when this great city of Philadelphia was one surging mass of patriots filling the air with the sounds of millions of shouts, a still small voice, hardly audible, and coming from a little disk of iron fastened to the center of a membrane, whispered into the ear of one of the judges at the exhibition, who was one of the greatest of living scientists, the tidings that a new revelation had descended upon mankind—that the swift and fiery messenger of Heaven's clouds had been harnessed to that delicate, tremorous,* and yet so potent form of energy called the Human Voice.

"The speaking telephone was born."

It is the golden jubilee of the telephone that America and mankind generally are commemorating in this year of 1926. Telephony's progress in the fifty years since its invention fairly staggers the imagination. Figures frequently fatigue. But there are romance and drama in those that tell the story of the telephone, and a power to awe, even in our age of monumental things.

On January 1, 1925, there were 26,038,508 telephones in the world. Of that number, sixty-two per cent., or roundly three-fifths, were in the United States, which is overwhelmingly the banner telephone country. Europe had twenty-six per cent.; all other countries put together, twelve per cent. The Scandinavian kingdoms are, telephonically, next to America, the most progressive in the world, and their inventors have made valuable contributions to the art.

---

*Berliner used the word *tremorous* subconsciously because it conveyed his precise meaning. Later it came to the attention of the *Century Dictionary*, and was incorporated in all subsequent editions of that lexicon, with credit to Berliner.

During the year 1924 the loquacious planet which civilized man inhabits and surcharges with language echoed to the thunder of 30,543,134,000 recorded and tabulated telephone conversations. Having the lion's share of telephones, Americans largely monopolized the world's thirty billion talks by wire. There is an average of over one telephone conversation daily for every three persons, men, women or children, in the United States. While we were holding twenty-one billion odd conversations, the rest of the world was conducting a beggarly nine billion odd. Following ourselves, the Germans and the Japanese were telephonically the most verbose peoples. China, or at least that portion of China still domiciled in Asia, does not figure in the official telephone statistics. The largest and most complete Chinese telephone exchange is in San Francisco. It is an artistic and architecturally exquisite little building, reminiscent of Cathay in its every nook and corner, and conducted by American-born Chinese girl operators who dress bewitchingly in native garb and lilt "hello" in the ancient accents of their ancestors. Nearly twenty thousand subscribers are served from their pagoda of palaver. San Francisco leads American cities in the number of telephones per each one hundred population. Perhaps Chinese capacity for conversation is responsible for giving the Golden Gate that distinction.

Nearly three-quarters of the world's telephone

systems are privately owned. About a quarter are comprised under government systems, such as Great Britain, France and Germany maintain. In the United States the overwhelming bulk of telephones is that embraced within the great coast-to-coast Bell System, in the eventual perfection of which the work of Emile Berliner played so essential a part. The Bell System has more contacts with the people of the country than any other single institution, not even excepting the United States Post-Office. Since it "hooked up" radio broadcasting stations with its continent-wide telephone and telegraph lines, its contacts can be calculated only in tens of millions. Bell lines connect with Canada and Cuba. In the two cities of New York and Chicago alone there are more telephones than in the four continents of Europe, Asia, Africa and South America combined. The 45,000,000 miles of wire in the Bell System would span the distance from the earth to the moon more than one hundred and forty times. So universal is the telephone that it has practically put the old "city directory" out of business. Anybody in hamlet, town or city worth looking up nowadays has his name in a telephone directory.

The financial aspect of American telephonic development is even more dazzling than the figures which record its physical expansion. So vast have become the holdings of the Bell System that a corporation entirely separate from the telephone company proper, the Bell Telephone Securities

Company, is now concerned with their administration. At its head is David F. Houston, who became the chancellor of the telephone exchequer after having been Secretary of the Treasury in President Wilson's Cabinet.

Mr. Houston directs the economics of a colossal organism. The number of stockholders in the Bell System (known on the New York stock exchange as the American Telephone and Telegraph Company) has grown from seven thousand five hundred in 1900 to more than three hundred and sixty-two thousand in 1926. About a sixth of the stockholders are Bell System employees. The total assets of the System on December 31, 1925 were $2,938,000,000. Telephone employees in the United States, including those engaged in making Bell apparatus, numbered on January 1, 1926, more than 335,189 (of whom 41,709 were on the payroll of the Western Electric Company). During 1925 more than 813,000 individual telephone installations were added to the Bell System. By the end of the year 16,720,000 telephones were inter-connected so that practically any one of them can be connected with any other one anywhere in the United States, day or night. Over 50,000,000 toll and exchange connections, each an individual transaction, are handled daily.

At the end of 1925 the Bell System's capital stock outstanding amounted to $921,597,000.* Net in-

---

*The capital stock of the "A. T. and T." was increased during the summer of 1926 to more than one billion dollars, making it probably the biggest corporation in the world, a distinction previously held by the United States Steel Corporation.

come during that year was $107,504,000, derived from gross earnings of $761,200,000. For more than forty-four years the American Telephone and Telegraph Company and its predecessor have paid dividends to the public, which owns its stock, of not less than seven and one-half dollars a share per annum. Since July, 1921, dividends have been at the rate of nine dollars a share. Telephone rates are, on the average, only thirty-three per cent. higher than ten years ago, while wages and material costs have increased at a considerably larger rate.

The genesis of these fabulous results, the material measure of the triumph of telephony's creators—whose were the hands and minds that enabled their fruition—the vision and the plodding that, between them, evolved conversational order out of acoustic chaos—the bitter controversies and heart-breaking, bankrupting litigation that dogged the footsteps of the pioneers—how despair, then victory, accompanied their labors in kaleidoscopic procession—that is now the story to be unfolded. Man's eternal struggle with the inscrutable is marked by few episodes so filled with drama.

CHAPTER VI

ALL inventions savor of the romantic, running the gamut that begins with inspiration, is marked by despair half-way, and ends in triumph. But there is no scientific miracle that outrivals the romance of the telephone.

Talking by telephone is nowadays so fundamental a part of human existence that we take it for granted, like the air we breathe, or the sky above us, or the flowers that bloom in the spring. We have come to regard the telephone, in other words, as a natural phenomenon that was always with God's children. Yet it celebrated its fiftieth birthday only in 1926. It is but a third of the age of our young republic.

In the invention of the telephone one name stands out like Mars at Perihelion—Alexander Graham Bell. Though the *idea* of a telephone was not original with Bell, no one anticipated him in actual achievement. His own discovery was utterly unique; his application of it, *scientifically* complete. It only remained for another to find *the missing link* in an otherwise flawless acoustic chain. That link

51

was a practical transmitter. Alexander Graham Bell was the *inventor* of the telephone. Emile Berliner was its *perfecter.*

The modern telephone is the joint product of their genius. History will bracket their names as those of men who dreamed their dreams in so providential proximity that mankind, with little delay, was able to avail itself of the boon of telephony. Emile Berliner's invention of the transmitter, to be dealt with in orderly sequence in succeeding chapters, has been called the jewel in the crown that Bell fashioned—the gem that gave it effective luster.

Charles Bourseuil, a Frenchman, was the first scientist of record to concern himself with the idea of sending speech by telegraph. In 1854, with unusual boldness, Bourseuil advanced the theory that two diaphragms, one operating an electric contact and the other under the influence of an electromagnet, might be employed for transmitting speech over long distances connected by wire. "Speak against one diaphragm," Bourseuil said, "and let each vibration *'make or break'* the electric contact. The electric pulsations thereby produced will set the other diaphragm working, and the latter ought then to reproduce the transmitted sound."

The Frenchman was credulous enough—his hypothesis must almost have subjected him to suspicions of lunacy—to believe that electricity could in some way be made to propel the human voice through space. Bourseuil's conception was intrinsically sound. He realized that if some electrical mechanism could be devised so flexible as to respond to all of the vibrations of sound, he would have a "telephone."

Bourseuil's ideas were exploited with avidity by European scientific journals, which reprinted them from the original French publications. Among the first to take note of them was a prominent German semi-weekly, *The Didaskalia,* published at Frankfort-on-the-Main. On September 28, 1854, it gave the earliest known expression to the term, "Electrical Telephony." Under that title *The Didaskalia* printed a full account of Bourseuil's fascinating thesis. Had his proposition not called for a "make and break" electric contact, the telephone might have been a reality long before Bell invented it. As things turned out, the Frenchman's theory led the early explorers in the new field astray. Bourseuil died without carrying out his ingenious idea.

Among Frankfort's institutes of learning was a Physical Society, which counted among its most zealous members an enthusiastic young teacher named Philip Reis, son of a poor baker. Reis constructed for himself a "telephone" embodying Bourseuil's conception. But it proved incapable of transmitting anything except the pitch of tones, or the pitch of speech. It could not transmit their quality. It produced nothing but a musical buzz. It never *talked*. Years afterward, Bell showed why. The reason was that you can not talk with *inter-*

rupted currents. You can talk only by *continuous
electric current,* which represents the undulations
of *waves of the voice* in all their minute shadings.

Emile Berliner never tires of recalling that when
Germans, twenty-five years later, read newspaper
accounts of Bell's invention of the telephone, they
flouted it as "an American exaggeration." They
asserted that Germany knew all about the Bourseuil-Reis apparatus and was certain there never
could be any such animal as a talking telephone.

The German language, which is rich in expressive idioms not easily translatable into English or
other tongues, boasts of the term *Rechthaberei*—the
state of being always and unquestionably right.
Germans wallowed in *Rechthaberei* when they heard
about Bell's telephone and Berliner's transmitter.
They said it simply "couldn't be done." Yet when
they were finally convinced that it *was* being done,
the Germans blithely claimed that *the telephone was
invented in Germany first!* When Philip Reis, the
baker's son was laid away, his epitaph read: "*Der
Erfinder des Telephons*"—inventor of the telephone. Reis was reported to have died in consequence of the sudden loss of the power of speech—
a dramatic end for a man who was undoubtedly on
the high road to achievement in the field of telephony.

Invention of the telegraph and the laying of the
Atlantic cable gave natural and irresistible impetus
in America to the next stage in sound transmis-

sion—telephony. In an insignificant shop in cultured Boston a tall, raw-boned Scotsman, not yet thirty, was grappling more or less blindly with a device he termed a harmonic telegraph. "He was wholly absorbed in the making of a nondescript machine, a sort of crude harmonica with a clock-spring reed, a magnet, and a wire," says Herbert N. Casson, in his *History of the Telephone*, published in 1922. "It was a most absurd toy in appearance. It was unlike any other thing that had ever been made in any country."

The plodding Scotsman was a young professor of the laws of speech. His name was Alexander Graham Bell. Born at Edinburgh in 1847, he pursued the calling of three generations of his forebears. The first Alexander Graham Bell won distinction as the creator of a method for overcoming stammering and other defects of the vocal organs. His descendant, Alexander Melville Bell, became an elocutionist of renown and invented a remarkable sign language which he named "Visible Speech." It was to be the destiny of the third Bell—Alexander Graham—to give supreme expression to the ancestral talent for improvement of speech by inventing the telephone. "Graham," Casson sets forth in his gripping story of the telephone, "inherited the peculiar genius of his fathers, both inventive and rhetorical, to such a degree that as a boy he had constructed an artificial skull, from gutta-percha and India rubber, which, when enliv-

ened by a blast of air from a hand-bellows, would
actually pronounce several words in an almost human manner!"

The Bell family emigrated to Canada in quest
of a climate more invigorating than that of Scotland, where two of Alexander Graham's brothers
had succumbed to the white plague. He himself was
threatened with the dread malady, and undoubtedly
owed his escape to his early life on the North
American plains. There, near Brantford, Ontario,
he recuperated while teaching "visible speech" to
Mohawk Indians. In 1875 Bell was making his living in Boston as a teacher of "visible speech" to
deaf mutes. But, as a thorough student of the correct theory of the telephone, his absorbing ambition was to convert it into a workable, practical
utility. That was the ultimate goal of his toyings
with the harmonic telegraph idea in the machine-
shop off Scollay Square. "If," Bell once explained
in the early stages of his experiments, "I could
make a current of electricity vary in intensity, precisely as the air varies in density during the production of a sound, I should be able to transmit speech
telegraphically." Along that line he steadfastly
carried on. Meantime he provided satisfactorily for
the creature comforts by maintaining a "School of
Vocal Physiology." But as enthusiasm to plumb
the bottomless mystery of telephony waxed, the
number of his pupils dwindled. At length, two deaf
mute girls, Mabel Hubbard (whom Bell afterward

married) and Georgie Sanders, with whose uncle and aunt the young professor now lived, became the principal source of his pedagogical income.

The Sanders home was in Salem, scene of early American "witchcraft." The cellar of the house was Bell's laboratory and workshop for three industrious years. There, amid batteries, magnets, tuning forks, wire, trumpets and what-not, he tinkered and adventured in hermit-like seclusion. The canny Scot in him feared possible discovery and theft of his ideas.

Bell, having determined that "if I can make a deaf mute talk, I can make iron talk," resorted to the most outlandish recourses to promote his experiments. He cajoled a medical friend to amputate an ear from a corpse, together with its internal parts, in order that Bell might use the human aural mechanism in tests with his acoustical apparatus.

The conception and subsequent invention of the speaking telephone, while the latter was based on an accidental discovery, was the logical result of Bell's preparatory studies in acoustics and of his innate capacity instantly to recognize the supreme importance of what suddenly happened—an "exceedingly faint sound which to other men might have been as inaudible as silence itself," says Casson, "but to Bell was a thunderclap."

CHAPTER VII

B ELL'S activities in 1875 were carried on in the attic of a five-story building at No. 109 Court Street, Boston. There was situated the electrical workshop of Charles Williams, manufacturer of telegraphic instruments. It was the Mecca of aspiring inventors, men of vast dreams and meager funds, who came to Williams to have the offspring of their visions incubated into brass and iron. One of these dreamers was Alexander Graham Bell. A mechanic in Williams' shop was another young man of Scotch ancestry, Thomas A. Watson, who was assigned to fashion Bell's apparatus. Later Watson became Bell's assistant. Thenceforward they worked together in the Court Street attic till the hour of triumph.

Bell had just reached the age of twenty-nine when on March 7, 1876, the United States Patent Office issued his patent, No. 174,465—since described as *"the most valuable single patent ever issued"* in the world. It was so uniquely ingenious an invention that it couldn't be called by any recognizable name. Bell himself, groping wholly in the dark, christened it "an improvement in telegraphy."

But with the granting of his patent Bell's experiments, with Watson's faithful assistance, continued intensively. Watson's own story of their collaboration is told in his *Birth and Babyhood of the Telephone*—an address delivered before the third annual convention of the Telephone Pioneers of America at Chicago in 1913:

"On the afternoon of June 2, 1875, we were hard at work on the same old job, testing some modification of the instruments. Things were badly out of tune that afternoon in that hot garret, not only the instruments, but, I fancy, my enthusiasm and my temper, though Bell was as energetic as ever.

"I had charge of the transmitters as usual, setting them squealing one after the other, while Bell was retuning the receiver springs one by one, pressing them against his ear as I have described. One of the transmitter springs I was attending to stopped vibrating and I plucked it to start it again. It didn't start and I kept on plucking it, when suddenly I heard a shout from Bell in the next room, and then out he came with a rush, demanding, 'What did you do then? Don't change anything. Let me see!'

"I showed him. It was very simple. The make-and-break points of the transmitter spring I was trying to start had become welded together, so that when I snapped the spring the circuit had remained unbroken while that strip of magnetized steel by its vibration over the pole of its magnet, was generating that marvelous conception of Bell's—a current of electricity that varied in intensity precisely as the air was varying in density within hearing distance of that spring.

"That wave-like undulatory current had passed through the connecting wire to the distant receiver which, fortunately, was a mechanism that could transform that current back into an extremely faint echo of the sound of the vibrating spring that had generated it, but what was still more fortunate, the right man had that mechanism at his ear during that fleeting moment, and instantly recognized the transcendent importance of that faint sound thus electrically transmitted.

"The shout I heard and his excited rush into my room were the result of that recognition. *The speaking telephone was born at that moment.*

"Bell knew perfectly well that the mechanism that could transmit all the complex vibrations of one sound could do the same for any sound, even that of speech. That experiment showed him that the complex apparatus he had thought would be needed to accomplish that long dreamed result was not at all necessary, for here was an extremely simple mechanism operating in a perfectly obvious way, that could do it perfectly.

"All the experimenting that followed that discovery, up to the time the telephone was put into practical use, was largely a matter of working out the details. We spent a few hours verifying the discovery, repeating it with all the differently tuned springs we had, and before we parted that night Bell gave me directions for making the first electric speaking telephone."

How real telephone history later was inaugurated is recorded by Watson in a few simple words that deserve immortality:

"I had gone to the Exeter Place rooms one evening to help Bell test some improvement and to spend the night with him. The occasion had not been arranged or rehearsed, as I suspect the send-

ing of the first message over the Morse telegraph
was arranged years before. Instead of that noble
first   telegraphic   message—'What   hath   God
wrought'—the first message of the telephone was:
'Mr. Watson, please come here, I want you!' "

That was on March 10, 1876. It was the first
complete sentence ever spoken and understood over
the telephone. Although perfection was still invis-
ibly remote, Bell and Watson had seen a great light.
During the summer of 1876 matters moved more
rapidly with them. How grateful Bell was for small
favors in the form of gradual progress is quaintly
admitted by Watson, who observed that "the telephone was talking so well that *one didn't have to
ask the other man to say it over again more than
three or four times before one could understand
quite well, if the sentences were simple.*"

It was the summer of the great Centennial at
Philadelphia. Through the influence of Gardiner
G. Hubbard, the father of Mabel Hubbard, the deaf
mute to whom Bell had taught "visible speech" and
who was now his sweetheart, the young inventor
gained fortuitous access to the exposition. Hubbard, a Centennial Commissioner from Massachusetts, arranged for Bell to exhibit his telephone in
some obscure waste space in the Education Department. There, on a plain table standing between a
stairway and a wall, the mechanism that was to
revolutionize mankind's activities first peeped forth.
No violet was ever more shrinking.

Romance took Bell to the Centennial, and Chance brought about his recognition there. By the merest accident of good fortune, the exposition judges had planned a special trip of inspection through the Department of Education for the first Sunday Bell was in Philadelphia. Hearing of the tour, Gardiner G. Hubbard, a patriarch of a man with flowing white hair and a beard that draped almost his whole chest, successfully pleaded with the judges to tarry for a moment at the hole in the wall where Bell's telephone apparatus was on display. It had been there, unheralded and unnoticed, for the better part of six weeks.

Amid the myriad of novelties with which the great Centennial was crowded, neither officials nor visitors had dignified the telephone with anything except passing attention; and hardly that. Nobody at all had the faintest realization that this crude contraption had already given forth a tinkle destined one day to roar around the civilized globe.

A hot Philadelphia afternoon had gone and sundown come, when, along about seven o'clock, the judges, who must have been conscientious souls, finally put in an appearance, frazzled by the heat, fatigued by their miles of meanderings through the exhibition buildings, and on the verge of surrender to the inner man, for it was past dinner-time. Bell pondered that they were in anything but ideal mood to pass considered judgment upon his poor thing of brass and wood and reeds. His fears were not groundless. With a gesture of indifference bordering on contempt, one of the judges picked up one of Bell's receivers and replaced it on the table with a bored grimace. Another judge indulged in what we moderns call a "wise crack," bringing comic relief into the situation, with the abashed young inventor as the butt.

Then it was Chance intervened, clad in imperial robes. The Centennial's most august visitors were the Emperor Dom Pedro de Alcantara, of Brazil, and his consort, the Empress Theresa, doomed, thirteen years later, to be dethroned by a revolution and to spend the rest of their saddened lives in banishment and exile. Casson terms what now ensued a fit setting for a chapter in *The Arabian Nights Entertainments*. Their Brazilian majesties, at the head of a retinue of courtiers and Centennial officials, happened at that late hour to be making one of their periodical promenades through the exposition grounds and buildings. They sauntered quite casually into the room where Bell's telephone was on exhibition. To the consternation of the inventor, his friends and the jury of mocking judges, Dom Pedro strode straight toward Bell, held out both hands to him, and said: "Professor Bell, I am delighted to see you again!"

Had the roof of the building suddenly caved in, or the floor sunk beneath them, neither Bell nor the judges could have been more thunderstruck. It must be remembered that, till that moment, Alexander Graham Bell was an utterly unknown inventor, like thousands who were tempting Fate and wooing the goddess of Fortune at the Centennial. In its voluminous catalogue they were merely numbers, and Exhibits A, B. C, etc. Bell was momentarily at a loss to account for the Brazilian Emperor's unfeigned cordiality and unmistakable acquaintance with him. Then it suddenly dawned upon him that Dom Pedro a couple of years before had observed Bell teaching a class of mutes at Boston University, and, largely in admiration of the "Bell system" of visible speech, later established an institute for the deaf at Rio de Janeiro.

Royalty now altered the whole atmosphere of the stuffy quarters in which the Bell telephone was tucked away. The judges were no longer jocular or apathetic. They were standing up and taking notice. Dom Pedro was fascinated by Bell's simple story of what he had invented. The Emperor, though he was from Brazil, and not Missouri, asked to be shown. Bell had a wire running across the room. At the transmitter end he himself took up station, having requested Dom Pedro to place the receiver to his ear on the other side of the room. An awesome silence reigned while the entire party, a group of fifty or more, waited, a little incredulously, for something to happen. Then suddenly, and excitedly, with a typical Latin gesture of animated emotion and astonishment, the Brazilian Emperor cried aloud: *"My God! It talks!"*

Bell next invited Professor Joseph Henry, the oldest scientist present, to take the receiver. Henry was the acknowledged authority on electrical science in the United States. He evolved the theory of a telephone before Bell's birth in the Scottish highlands half a century before. In 1875 Bell borrowed money to journey from Salem to Washington for a consultation with Henry, whom he found generously helpful and encouraging. Henry told Bell that the young inventor, his junior by fifty years, was "in possession of the germ of a great invention."

Bell lamented his lack of electrical knowledge. "Get it," said Henry. Bell said afterward those two words proved a life-time of inspiration to him.

After Professor Henry, Britain's great savant, then Sir William Thomson, later Lord Kelvin, and recognized throughout the world as the most eminent living electrical authority, was invited to undergo the sensational experience of telephone talk. Thomson a few years before had functioned triumphantly as engineer of the first Atlantic cable. When he turned from Bell's receiver, he affirmed, enthusiastically: "It *does* speak. It is the most wonderful thing I have seen in America!"

Bell and his telephone had now "arrived." Henry and Thomson were both judges. That they would heartily confer upon the invention the coveted Certificate of Award was no longer a matter of doubt. In their subsequent official reports they frankly registered their early skepticism and as unreservedly conceded their complete conversion. "Mr. Bell has achieved a result of transcendent scientific interest," wrote Sir William Thomson. "I heard his instrument speak distinctly several sentences. . . . I was astonished and delighted. . . . It is the greatest marvel hitherto achieved by the electric telegraph."

Darkness had long superseded dusk that humid Philadelphia Sunday afternoon at the Centennial before the judges were tempted to desert Bell's telephone. Alternately they talked and listened—literally, for hours. Next day the telephone was transported in triumph from its humble place in Education Hall to the judges' pavilion. There it remained enthroned for the rest of the Centennial, the magnet that drew scientists and visitors in jostling throngs. Overnight it had become "the star of the Centennial."

"It had been given no more than eighteen words in the official catalogue," says Casson, "and here it was acclaimed as the wonder of wonders. It had been conceived in a cellar and born in a machine-shop; and now, of all the gifts that our young American Republic had received on its one hundredth birthday, the telephone was honored as the rarest and most welcome of them all."

CHAPTER VIII

BERLINER SETS TO WORK

BY THE time the Centennial had passed into history, leaving America in a state of national exaltation over her glorious past and illimitable future, Emile Berliner was at work again in Washington. His job was that of a bookkeeper in the Seventh Street store, but it was not his pre-occupation. "Long, long thoughts" filled his head, and they were far remote from debits and credits. He had passed his twenty-fifth birthday. He had taken out American citizenship first papers. He had become thoroughly infected with the creative spirit that saturated the country. His studies in acoustics and electricity turned his attention naturally to the subject of telephony. The new science was a matter of popular discussion because of newspaper accounts, but few had ever seen a telephone, let alone speak through one. Even Berliner himself had never had a look at a telephone instrument.

Unmistakably, as the impending development of Emile Berliner's bent was to show, the young man was an inventor by nature or intuition. It was to demonstrate that a man may even possess a scientific instinct without knowing it. Berliner had an unquenchable longing to do something in the scientific field into which ambition was leading him, but he had no glimmer of realization that in him lay dormant talent which would ultimately spur ambition to the point of stellar achievement. Thus without anything savoring of trained equipment, premeditation or conscious purpose, Berliner's mind now drifted steadily along the uncharted course to which the wizardry of telephony pointed.

It would not do to say that Berliner was merely toying with the problems which electrical sound-transmission raised in his inquisitive thoughts, for he was deeply impressed by its mysteries and profound possibilities. But in the post-Centennial winter that found him drudging in a bookkeeper's cage at the back of a little store in Washington, Berliner's scientific activities were mainly confined to dreaming and speculating. He had a vague notion that somewhere along electrical lines a career would eventually open for him. It is no disparagement of the reputations which many inventors have won to say that predilection and accident are often among the factors upon which they were built. Could the annals of scientific achievement be traced to their source, it would undoubtedly be discovered that more than one dizzy height was scaled by means of chance abetting genius at a psychological moment. Lady Luck has played a star rôle throughout the

whole drama of mankind's unceasing evolution. But
it is only the intense mind, prepared to recognize the
accidental when it happens, that turns it to account.
Such was the mentality of Emile Berliner.

James J. Storrow, Sr., of Boston, one of the
most brilliant patent lawyers America ever produced, then counsel for the Bell Telephone interests,
once made a study of the psychological conditions
out of which inventors and inventions are developed.
He found that far more original ideas occur to inventors between the ages of twenty-one and twenty-
eight years than at any other period. Berliner, in
the midst of his twenty-sixth year, was immersed in
the consuming aspiration to make something of
himself in physical science in general, and in the
magic field of the speaking telephone in particular.
To become identified with this new industry as a
worker in it, rather than to give it new direction
in any pioneering sense, was his primary desire.
It amounted to a determination. He sensed that
telephony was "the coming thing." He wanted to
be on the ground floor of its development, and grow
up with it.

In 1910 Emile Berliner, addressing the Telephone Society of Washington, gave an amusing account of the conditions amid which he set to experimental telephonic work in the bleak midwinter
of 1876-1877.

"I lived in Washington, as I do now," he said,
"and there was one little store that dealt in electri-

cal goods, the store of Mr. George C. Maynard. It
was on G Street, between Fourteenth and Fifteenth
Streets—a little bit of a store. It contained a few
keys and sounders and bluestone batteries (they did
not have any others, to speak of) and some relays
and some tapes, and some wire, and probably one
or two more highly scientific coils and galvano-
meters. But that was all. That comprised the
electrical stores of Washington.

"There was no commercial electric light, but
there was at the Capitol, near the dome upstairs, a
large room in which was a big battery consisting
of about one hundred so-called Smee cells. At that
time these were very well known among scientific
men. Each consisted of a jar full of sulphuric acid
and water, a piece of carbon and a piece of zinc.
That was a Smee cell. Of course, you know it
polarized, weakened, very quickly. Every Fourth of
July the daily papers announced: 'To-night the electric light will be shown from the Capitol,' and everybody was down on Pennsylvania Avenue after dark
to see it. All at once we would see a brilliant arc
light at the lower part of the dome. The electrician
was at work. By and by it went out because the
battery polarized, and then we had to wait about
twenty minutes or a half-hour for another glimpse
of the shining electric light. It was quite an interesting exhibition, and everybody enjoyed it very
highly.

"There were no dry cells known in those days
and there was no electric bell. The house bells
were mechanical. Iron bell wire was used, and
every blacksmith, or every locksmith, knew how to
fix the house bell, and from time to time the wire
would stretch, or something of the kind, and they
had all kinds of trouble with the bell. Of course, it
was a pretty good-sized bell, and gave the old-time
jingle such as you hear now and then in boarding-
houses.

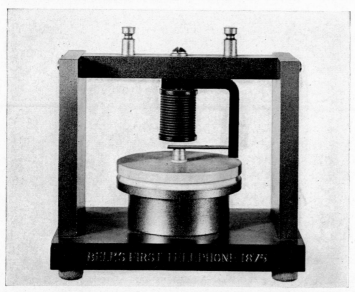

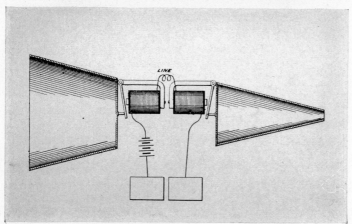

FIRST BELL TELEPHONE, JUNE, 1875

BELL'S MAGNETO SYSTEM, 1876

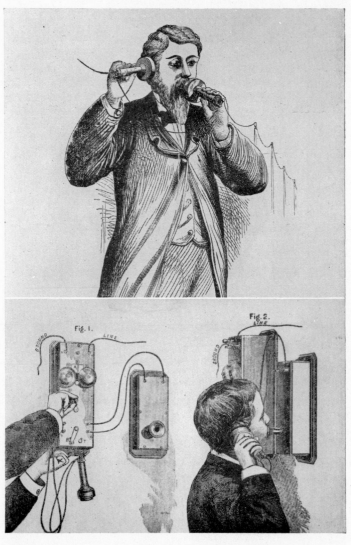

BELL'S MAGNETO TELEPHONE, 1877. (CONTEMPORARY ILLUSTRATION)

BELL'S MAGNETO TELEPHONE SYSTEM IN 1877

"Then there were horse-cars, no electric cars. Afterward they had the cable-car, and one day, the power-house was burned, and they had to supply horses for the cars. I recall how I once had the privilege of riding up to Mt. Pleasant in a mule car. They got the mules over in Alexandria to help out. Of course, it required some time to get around, but people had plenty of time then. If you wanted anything, you had to send a messenger, and you could attend to only two or three transactions a day, where you can now attend to a hundred with the aid of the telephone.

"There was but one electrical paper in the United States. That was the official organ of the Western Union Telegraph Company, and known as the *Journal of the Telegraph*. It came out once a month as a sort of pamphlet. Such were the conditions in 1876."

Berliner was living in a room on the third floor of a typical, middle-class Washington brick dwelling of the era, situated at No. 812 Sixth Street, N. W., and just around the corner from the Behrend store. Though plainly furnished, the house was neatly kept by a widow and her two half-grown children, who were engaged in the time-honored business of "taking lodgers." Berliner's quarters soon came to look and smell like an electrical laboratory. He filled the place with wires, batteries and other paraphernalia. Presently he rigged up a set of "telephones" between his window and the barn. Another series of animated wires led to the living quarters of his landlady and her family, who were duly pressed into Berliner's experimental service.

The house at No. 812 Sixth Street still stands. When Emile Berliner visited it not long ago, with a party of friends interested in seeing his first workshop, the present occupant was astonished to learn that she inhabits so historic premises. But she returned coincidence for surprise, when Berliner told her of the establishment's epochal place in telephony, for, she said, "I have three daughters and two sons-in-law, they all work for the telephone company, and my late husband himself was an inventor! His name was Frank Howarth Brown and he devised the sorts caster for making type." The widow thought her home might well aspire to be known as "Telephone House." It was not long afterward that *The Transmitter,* house organ of the Chesapeake and Potomac Telephone Company in Washington, having had its attention called to the quaint history of the lodging-house in Sixth Street, devoted an illustrated article to it. As "Telephone House" it now takes its place in historic Washington.

Berliner had not seen the Bell membrane telephone at the Centennial and began tinkering with speech-transmission much as you play blind man's buff—without knowing at all where you're going. He thought that the proper way to transmit speech was by means of battery current. That fundamental seemed clear to him. Bell had made his invention with the magnetic current, but Berliner thought it might be possible to do it differently, so before the Bell process was understood except by a limited number of scientists, Berliner set out on unexplored paths of his own. Spare time during the working day and all of his evening time, till sleep claimed him, found him scheming and plodding, wondering and thinking, with his interest in the electric mysteries growing with every unrequited experiment.

Presently it occurred to Berliner that he could take a diaphragm and a contact-pin, or screw, touching it in the center, and somehow produce an undulatory, wave-like electric current by continuous action of the contact, that is to say, not by interrupting it, but by some form of perpetuity. "I did not catch on to the pressure principle right away," he explains, "but I thought that if I took a flat spring and attached that to a screw, I could adjust the spring against the diaphragm—the current, of course, passing across the contact—so that if I spoke against it, each vibration would bring a little broader surface of the spring against the diaphragm and thereby produce electric sound waves in the current."

That was Berliner's first crude idea. He gave it form and substance by patching up a flimsy sort of "telephone," which consisted of a membrane and a piece of spring in front. But he found he could not transmit speech. No discernible action ensued. Berliner now realized, probably for the first time, that his technical knowledge was unequal to the development of a conception that was inherently and scientifically sound. Then Fate intervened. It guided his steps in a fruitful direction.

Berliner had struck up an acquaintance with Mr. Alvan S. Richards, chief operator at the Washington fire-alarm telegraph office, which the former visited occasionally. In those archaic times, forty-nine years ago, fire-alarm systems were as primitive as everything else in America was. The Washington fire telegraph office was filled with the usual jumble of instruments, alarm-bells and old-fashioned blue-stone cells or batteries. During one of his visits, Berliner told Richards that, in connection with his amateur telephonic experiments, he was now interested in learning telegraphy, and had actually been practising at "sending."

"Come back and let me hear what you can do," said Richards.

The chief of the fire-alarm telegraph pointed to an instrument in disuse, and told his visitor he might try his hand at it. Berliner had but begun, when Richards interrupted to advise:

"Hold on, this isn't right. You must press down the key—not simply touch it."

"What difference does that make—whether I press the key down or not—so long as it makes a contact?" asked Berliner curiously.

"What you have to do," explained Richards, "is to make a firm contact, otherwise your message might not be readable at the receiving end." Then he explained that in long-distance transmission, where the resistance is high, the sending key must be pressed down rather forcibly if efficient reception is to be assured.

"That's why we use men exclusively for long-distance telegraphy," Richards added, "because they naturally press down hard. They have a strong touch. Women wouldn't naturally press down hard and are therefore not adaptable to long-distance work."

That clear explanation immediately sank into Berliner's mind. Quick as a flash, he rejoined:

"Do you mean to say that more current passes over that contact when I press hard?"

"Decidedly. That's exactly what I mean," was the reply.

"All right. Thanks. Good-by." And Berliner was off.

"I went home in a highly expectant mood," he has since recounted, in telling of what proved to be the turning point in Berliner's telephonic researches. "I knew I had it. Forthwith I rigged up a diaphragm, made a contact with a steel button, and polished it up so brightly as to insure a clean contact. Then I began to adjust it until the galvanometer showed the current. Then I pressed ever so gently. I found that each time I pressed against it the galvanometer deflected a larger angle. I then knew the principle was right."

Berliner saw through the microphonic principle

before he had worked it out with apparatus. The kernel of his discovery lay in the conception of its operation. All the rules of electricity theretofore forbade the microphone. The invariable rule in electro-magnets had been *firm contacts*. He had here *a loose contact* with its importance lying in the *variableness of the pressure,* which at once presented itself as something far more delicate than the abrupt make-and-break principle of the old and abandoned Bourseuil-Reis apparatus. Berliner was using Bell's undulatory idea, only he converted an already existing electric current of any strength *into waves, corresponding to sound waves with all their minute characteristics,* instead of letting the force of the voice *produce* a weak electric current as Bell's telephone did.

"It needs an abler pen than mine to do justice to the work that Emile Berliner did in improving the telephone," says Waldemar Kaempffert, engineer, patent attorney and one-time editor of the *Scientific American and Popular Science Monthly.* "Berliner was one of half-a-dozen men who saw the shortcomings of the early telephone transmitter. He improved it both acoustically and electrically— standardized it, in a word, so that it became ultimately the instrument it is to-day. The Courts of the United States have given Berliner the most ample credit for this achievement, after a thorough examination of what patent lawyers call 'the state of the art.' "

During the famous telephone litigation Mr. Storrow, the Bell Company's counsel, elucidating the Berliner discovery, said: "A thousand inventors have worked on telephones and five hundred of them on microphones. They have improved the details, but have not been able to supersede the Berliner type, so brilliant and daring was Berliner's conception."

Mr. Spottiswoode, a scientist of eminence and president of the British Association, stated in his inaugural address at Dublin in August, 1878: "It is remarkable that the gist of the (Berliner) invention seems to lie in obtaining and perfecting that which electricians have hitherto most scrupulously avoided—namely, loose contact."

Professor Barker, the United States government's expert in the futile litigation to annul Emile Berliner's patent, confessed in his testimony that the invention of the loose contact transmitter at one time passed the limits of scientific credibility. "If any man had come to me or to science, in 1877," said Barker, "and proposed the idea of the microphone, science would have said: 'We have no reason to believe that that is possible; that any material exists which will answer those purposes; that those slight forces will accomplish anything.' In short, I should have declared it impossible, and that, I think, would have been the judgment of all scientific men at the time."

Thus the microphone came to be—the instrument

which renders the faintest vibrations of sound audible, and, by varying the contact pressure, increases sound's intensity.

We shall now trace more minutely the steps which Berliner took to enable talkative Mother Earth to hold her thirty billion telephone conversations a year.

CHAPTER IX

FROM SOAP-BOX TO MICROPHONE

BELL'S telephone—"the star of the Centennial"—was simply a good receiver. It was a very poor transmitter, even for short distances. You talked into it and you listened for a reply from the same kind of instrument. When Emile Berliner set himself the task of making the Bell telephone practical for all distances, it was far from certain that what went into it as talk would come out as talk at the other end of the line. That which emerged was more often a jumble of sounds that was difficult to understand and had to be repeated. At best, it was necessary to shout the message, or clamp the lips on to the mouthpiece. Even then, it was a gamble whether the spoken words would be articulate. The talking itself produced the electric current that barely went over the wire. It was the so-called magneto-electric induction force, discovered by the celebrated Michael Faraday in Great Britain in 1831 that produced Bell's speaking current. That was the mile-post which marks the beginnings of Emile Berliner's researches—the studies that led to the employment of the much

79

stronger battery current, *thrown into undulations corresponding to speech,* and to his invention of the microphone.

Until the year 1877 dawned Berliner's experiments had partaken mainly of the theoretical. He was now ready to give them practical form by designing an apparatus embodying his conception of the microphone principle. What the inconspicuous young dry-goods clerk, still a virtual stranger in the land of his adoption, was on the verge of achieving was a battery speech transmitter, *the principle of which has never been changed or superseded.* Out of the humble lodging-house back room in Washington was about to come the magical little thing destined to link not only cities, but countries, and not only countries, but continents, and link not only continents but span the whole inhabited globe. To-day, forty-nine years after Queen Genius, in imagination, gave Emile Berliner the accolade and anointed him a knight of science, he pleads for a universal language which shall bind the nations as the telephone linked them. He believes it would end war, as the microphone, half a century ago, led to the annihilation of space.

Contemplate the miracle we are now dispassionately reviewing—no other term for it seems appropriate. The telephone was not yet in public use. Here was Berliner, under twenty-six, and utterly self-taught. He had no scintilla of the scientific background that predestined Alexander Graham

Bell for a career in acoustical communication. Yet the young Hanoverian-American was by way of giving the telephone its most vital and essential addition, the loose contact transmitter, or microphone, and the continuous current induction coil, or transformer. He was to do so, most incredible of all, within a few months from the time of starting actual experiments. Asked innumerable times—asked often to-day—how a man of his environment and complete lack of technical training managed to reach out into the infinite and, with the precision of a triphammer, hit almost instantaneously upon his objective, Emile Berliner confesses himself at a loss to explain.

Probably a gift for concentration, and, as trained physicists have termed it, a scientific instinct, come as near to clearing up the mystery as anything else. Concentration was automatic with him. He let no single day go by without pursuing his experiments. Every luncheon-hour at the store in Seventh Street would find Berliner snatching time to run around the corner to his "laboratory" lodgings. Either a few minutes of tinkering or a few moments of study—he allowed no time to go to waste. Sometimes he was up before the sun, restlessly eager to observe the further effects of the elusive electric current on a crude contraption which a carpenter friend had rigged up for him.

March 4, 1877, was a memorable day in Washington. Rutherford B. Hayes, Republican, was to be inaugurated President of the United States following an embittered contest with Samuel J. Tilden, Democrat, in the midst of which the grim specter of another American civil war more than once raised its menacing head. Hayes had been declared the duly elected chief magistrate of the republic, though by the slenderest possible margin in the Electoral College, and Washington, on Inauguration Day, was crammed with visitors in a state of excited expectancy. Among them were friends of Berliner who, visiting him, became so fascinated by what he was accomplishing in the magic new realm of communication that they forgot all about President-elect Hayes and the day's adventure—a trip to the east front of the United States Capitol for the inaugural ceremony—on which they had set out early in the morning.

The "miracle" that Berliner had to show them was the membrane of a toy drum with a common sewing needle firmly adjusted through it, a steel dress-button, and a guitar string—the chrysalis, though few believed it, of the telephone transmitter.

Early in April, 1877, Berliner made an iron diaphragm transmitter. He knocked the bottom out of a wooden soap-box; nailed on in place of it a piece of sheet-iron for a diaphragm, and placed a cross-bar across the middle of the box. A common screw, passing through this cross-bar, touched the center of the diaphragm. In fact, Berliner soldered a polished steel button to the end of the screw so that the button was the actual contact-piece which touched the diaphragm.

This was a great improvement. He tried it with a galvanometer and found that the current varied regularly with the variation of pressure. *With this he easily got speech.* The instruments were not perfect, certainly. But they talked; and they will talk to-day.

Berliner's soap-box was a receptacle seven by twelve inches in size. The labels that still adorn it tell the world that the original package contained "Old Brown Windsor Soap" made by the American Company, of Philadelphia. Undoubtedly it is the most famous soap-box in history, though nowadays we usually associate soap-boxes with street-corner agitators. To-day it occupies an honored niche in the United States National Museum along with other Berliner relics. Inside of it is tacked a card on which is printed:

Introduced in evidence in
Circuit Court of United States District
of Massachusetts
In Equity 3106:
U. S. A. vs. American Bell Telephone
Company and Emile Berliner
Defendants' exhibit.
Berliner's Soap-Box Transmitter.
M. S. C., Special Examiner.

There is fortunately a graphic record, in Emile
Berliner's own words, of the precise chain of events
that led up to this earliest, though epochal, achievement of his. It is taken from his unchallenged
testimony in the lawsuit brought by the Government
against Berliner's patent.

"On the eighth of April, 1877," he says, "late
in the evening I had connected the instrument of the
galvanometer I have previously described and I was
joining two terminal wires for the purpose of closing the circuit. It was exceedingly quiet about the
house and on the street. In closing the circuit, I
suddenly heard a noise coming from the diaphragm,
which surprised me greatly. I thought I had mis-
taken my ears, but on repeatedly making and breaking the circuit a distinct and sometimes loud tick
came from the diaphragm and apparently from the
point of contact between the diaphragm and the
steel ball.

"That was entirely new to me, and I became
much agitated, because I saw immediately that I had
here a new electrical phenomenon, viz.: that sound
was produced without the aid of electrical magnetism, merely by the current itself. I quickly took
a tuning-fork which I had in my possession; I wound
one of the wire terminals around the shank of the
tuning-fork, struck the same on the table and applied the vibrating prongs to the other terminal of
the line.

"Immediately a loud musical sound corresponding in pitch to the sound of the tuning-fork came
from the iron diaphragm. I knew at that moment
that I had made an important addition to my observations, for I quickly perceived that if the diaphragm could give out a musical sound, it could also
reproduce speech, when, instead of an interrupted
current, an undulatory one was sent to affect it.

"I also saw very plainly that I had here an apparatus which would act both as transmitter and receiver of articulate sound electrically; and that I had something analogous to that of Mr. Bell, who also used the same instrument both as transmitter and receiver, but something far simpler and cheaper.

"I had always been ambitious to have apparatus different from that of Mr. Bell, and while I perfectly well knew that I could not get around his undulatory current claims, still I thought it was something to have actually apparatus entirely different from his; and from that day I never touched again a Bell receiver until about a year afterward, but used a contact transmitter also as a receiving instrument.

"On the next day I got another soap-box, brought it to the carpenter and had it fixed up in the same way as my other one. It was ready on the next day. I tried it on the evening of April tenth in my own room to see if it also was sensitive to pressure, and showed these variations of the galvanometer needle; and on the next morning, before going to the store, I tried a practical experiment from my room to the room down-stairs, and made the ladies of the house listen.

"They were very greatly surprised when I transmitted as I always did, for the purpose of amusing them, by means of interrupted currents; they heard the tunes loudly from the soap-box all over the room, and when I made them listen close to the apparatus and transmitted speech by variation of pressure they reported to me much better results than they had previously heard in other experiments, and they also thought that it was very wonderful indeed. They recognized my voice, and got familiar sentences now and then.

"It was very difficult to adjust the apparatus. I had to run up-stairs and down-stairs continuously, both for adjusting the transmitter and receiver. The current would heat the contact, the plate would bulge off a little and get out of adjustment; but we did get quite good results.''

While it is easy to explain the action of the microphone by increase and decrease of pressure between two electrodes, it is not so easy to understand why a loose contact should transmit speech electrically, or in other words why an electric current can be thrown into waves corresponding to sound waves in all their delicacies through the medium of a loose contact by means of variable pressure.

Several theories were advanced by scientists to explain the action at the loose contact. But Berliner himself very early gave the only explanation that would stand scientific criticism. His theory was that a loose contact between two electrodes, or ends of conducting wires, is no real contact, but that a thin stratum or layer of air intervenes, and that this is the field of action where the voice vibrations with all their delicate differences are transformed into electric vibrations exactly corresponding to the voice.

Let the reader consider that air is a conductor of electricity precisely as is a metal wire. It does not readily carry as much current, but, being very elastic, it is highly adaptable to microphonic action.

That there exists a layer of air between two electrodes in loose contact with each other has been proved in two ways, one by Berliner himself. He placed a loose contact, held together by light spring pressure, in a closed box which was connected to an air pump that could exhaust the air from that box. Careful and repeated measurements showed that more current passed over the contact when the air was exhausted; or, putting it more scientifically, the electrical resistance of the contact was lower in a vacuum than in air. The proof offered by others than Berliner consisted of looking through a loose contact with a powerful tele-microscope, when it was found that there was a thin gap between the two electrodes and that they did not actually touch each other.

Therefore, it will be seen that when sound strikes the diaphragm, which actuates the loose contact in a microphone, it changes the thickness of that thin layer of air at each vibration and the electric current which passes is therefore thrown into electric vibrations corresponding to the sound waves. It may correspondingly be a surprise to some, to learn that the term "talking on the air," so commonly used by broadcasters to-day, is more scientifically correct than is popularly realized.

The curious receiving action of the loose contact has never been fully clarified. According to Emile Berliner's *caveat* of 1877, it is due to a force of repulsion at the contact, which is *variable* according to the strength of the passing current.

CHAPTER X

NOW we approach an episode in the life of Emile Berliner that brands him, perhaps as much as any single achievement in his whole career, as a favored child of genius. Before he went to bed on the night of April 8, 1877, he made the rough draft of a *caveat* describing the telephonic results he had just achieved. Four days later he made a clean copy of the draft. Then he determined, without either legal or scientific aid, to conduct his own negotiations with the United States Patent Office covering the invention of the microphone. Under the former patent laws of the United States, a *caveat* was a description of an invention designed to be patented, lodged in the Patent Office before the patent itself was applied for. It operated as a bar to other applications respecting the same invention. Modern manufacturing corporations employ the great brains of the patent-law profession at fancy fees to draw their patent documents.

Filing a *caveat* did not imply that the inventor considered his invention incomplete in the legal sense, but at most that he hoped to improve its form

88

of embodiment. The patent statute speaks of "a person who makes any new invention or discovery, and desires time to mature the same." The person has "made" the invention, but more mature thought is eventually to apply the finishing touches. Berliner was experimenting in that direction.

His financial condition at this time was such that he did not hesitate to avail himself of the privilege of drawing his own *caveat,* at a cost of ten dollars, instead of filing an application, which would have cost at least sixty dollars. Think of the plight of the man who facilitated the perfection of modern telephony, having to hesitate between the advisability of taking by himself a legal step of transcendent importance, because it was cheap, or hiring an expert to do it for him at a cost of fifty dollars more!

As a matter of fact, Berliner's economic state required him to resort to every possible economy. Describing his plight at that time, in the course of the subsequent telephone litigation, Berliner said:

"I had contracted some debts in 1876, in New York, which had not been fully paid when I returned to Washington. In the few months I was out of a job I had not earned anything at all. My place as bookkeeper brought me fifteen dollars a week, or something of that kind. I don't remember exactly the wages I had in the latter part of 1876 at Mr. Behrend's store in Washington, but I was out of a position for a couple of months on account of the failure of my employer. After that I earned an average of about twelve dollars a week with Mr. Behrend.''

Later, during the same testimony, Berliner testified that while he was employed in the Fahlberg laboratory at New York, he was paid six dollars a week, and had to leave that work because Fahlberg could not afford to pay him more.

Berliner's *caveat* was filed and dated April 14, 1877. Obviously non-superstitious, he had sworn to it the day previous, April thirteenth. It was composed and written entirely by himself, without outside aid of any character whatsoever. He had familiarized himself with the terminology of the Patent Office on such occasions, but scorned the services of a patent attorney. The preamble of the Berliner *caveat* read:

> The petition of Emile Berliner, of the City of Washington, in the District of Columbia, respectfully represents:
>
> That he has made certain Improvements in Electrical Telegraphy, or Telephony, and that he is now engaged in making experiments for the purpose of perfecting the same, preparatory to applying for Letters Patent therefor. He therefore prays that the subjoined description of his invention may be filed as a *caveat** in the confidential archives of the Patent Office.
>
> EMILE BERLINER,
> 818 Seventh Street, N. W.

*See Appendix for full text of *Caveat*.

It was followed by the statutory "Specification," of which the following opening paragraph tells the story of the microphone in a nutshell:

"Part I. The following is a description of my newly-invented apparatus for transmitting sound of any kind by means of a wire or any other conductor of electricity, to any distance.

"It is a fact and a scientific principle that objects near each other which are charged with electricity of the same polarity repel each other. It is also a fact that if at a point of contact between two ends of a galvanic current, the pressure between both sides of the contact becomes weakened, the current passing becomes intense, as, for instance, if an operator on a Morse instrument does not press down the key with a certain firmness, the sounder at the receiving instrument does work much weaker than if the full pressure of the hand would have been used. Based on these two facts, I have constructed a simple apparatus for transmitting sound along a line of a galvanic current in the following manner, etc."

James J. Storrow, chief counsel for the Bell Telephone Company and in his day without a superior as a patent lawyer, and with few peers, thus eulogized Berliner's *caveat*, which, from the hour of its submission, ranked as one of the most remarkable documents ever filed with the United States Patent Office:

"This now classical document, unrivaled for its concise accuracy and completeness, worthy to rank with Bell's patent (drawn also by the inventor himself) was the unaided production of this young man of twenty-five. It is impossible not to feel that Berliner had made the invention and matured the subject, and that he realized its importance. It was no vague and half-formed idea, of the sort that men abandon. No one ever throws away so perfect an offspring of his brain. There is one passage in it, which of itself is enough to prove that it was the result, not of thought alone, but of thought carried out by experiment.''

Mr. Joseph Lyons, assistant examiner of electricity in the electrical division of the Patent Office from 1880 to 1885, testifying during the telephone litigation, said:

"When I came into the electrical division (December, 1880), I asked for information on the particular point of whether anybody had anticipated Emile Berliner in the invention of the microphone, and I found that all assistant examiners in the room with one voice declared Mr. Berliner as the first inventor of the microphone. Under such circumstances, I was not in a condition to question the fact, and, moreover, I found among the records of the office Mr. Berliner's *caveat* of April, 1877, which described a microphone in such clear and unmistakable terms that there could be no question about it."

The new departure in Emile Berliner's experiments set the pace and charted the direction for his future work in telephony. Now realizing that he had something different from Bell's telephone, he labored unceasingly to improve the loudness of the loose contact as a receiver. It was not until many months later that he came into possession of a modern Bell instrument and was able to notice that the loose contact was so wonderfully sensitive a transmitter.

For a time the Bell magneto telephone remained in obscurity. The country talked of it more or less vaguely and the newspapers wrote about it, but people never listened over a telephone, or ever saw one. For the most part Bell's invention was coming to be looked upon as a plaything. Now and then men would sheepishly confess their unwillingness to "make fools of themselves" by leaning against a wall and talking into a wooden box with no apparent result except a metallic echo of their own voice!

Little progress in the new art seemed to be in sight. All of a sudden came the sensational announcement that Bell's telephones were now being used over longer distances and that some people in Massachusetts were actually using the telephone for inter-communication between their houses!

But Emile Berliner was still in Washington waiting for his opportunity.

CHAPTER XI

NEARLY everybody who is interested in radio knows that the two vital instruments necessary for broadcasting are the microphone and the so-called transformers. They are parts of the vast inheritance which radio has received from telephony. Both of these were conceived and used by Emile Berliner for sending the voice by electricity in the spring of 1877. He discovered that the carrying power of the microphone could be much enhanced by combining an induction coil in circuit with it.

In the practical arts it is always the aim of the scientific man to work with simple means and with the least expense. Thus, if it is possible to operate a telephone transmitter with one or two cells of battery, it is superfluous to apply a powerful dynamo current or a battery of one hundred cells. Berliner was far-sighted enough to take these requirements into consideration. Within a month of the time he had worked out the microphone, he evolved the idea of adding the highly important transformer.

94

In those early years, the transformer was known as an induction coil or inductorium. It transforms currents of low voltage or low electric pressure into high voltage or high electric pressure. In the vernacular, as used even by telephone people, the transformer "boosts" the current. Before Berliner's application of the transformer to telephony, transformer induction coils were employed only for making sparks, giving shocks, showing the luminous effects of the electric current in vacuum tubes, and setting off mines containing explosive mixtures. For all these purposes, a battery current was passed through the inner coil, or primary, of heavy wire, and when this battery current was suddenly interrupted a spark jumped from one end of the secondary or outer coil, which was wound around the inner primary coil, to the other end or terminal of the secondary.

In April and May, 1877, Berliner, who had no trained assistant to help him, had to run incessantly from one end of the line to the other when his crude contact telephones did not work well. It was correspondingly difficult for him to readjust the delicate contacts in order to make them work satisfactorily. Being fully familiar with the induction coil, he conceived the idea of putting one of his instruments with a small battery into the primary coil of an inductorium at one station and the second instrument, which was at the other end of the line, with a small battery, into the primary of another inductorium. The secondary coils of both inductoria he connected to the line.

This arrangement made each of the contact instruments independent of the other and greatly facilitated keeping them well adjusted. Incidentally it foreshadowed what afterward became common practise in practical telephony.

It is also an historic fact that this was the first time that any induction coil or transformer was ever used with undulatory, continuous currents. This usage became the prototype of all subsequent transformers used by the million in power stations, electric light plants, and, to-day, in radio. The microphone and continuous current transformer, both invented by Emile Berliner forty-nine years ago, are indispensable to the science of broadcasting, and probably always will be. It goes without saying that transformers used in telephony operate by means of Berliner's continuous current system.

Two weeks after Berliner filed his *caveat* in the United States Patent Office in April, 1877, describing the microphone, Thomas A. Edison filed a patent application describing a transmitter in which a metal diaphragm vibrated against a large flat disk covered with graphite, a form of carbon. The action consisted in bringing a larger or smaller area of the graphited disk in touch with the diaphragm at each vibration. In the following year Mr. Edison developed his compressed lampblack button, which acted by increase and decrease of internal pressure

on the lampblack. But it was Berliner who during
the summer of 1877 first used a hard carbon microphone precisely as such contacts have always been
used by the Bell Telephone Company and later in
the radio microphone. Multiple contacts introduced
later were mentioned by Berliner in his *caveat* of
April 14, 1877.

The modern telephone transmitter, or microphone, of which the radio microphone is only a
larger form, contains a box filled with granules of
hard carbon, each in loose contact with one another.
It is noteworthy that, foreseeing this possibility,
Berliner's *caveat* said: "There may be more than
one point of contact becoming effected by the same
vibrations."

Berliner, now having achieved continuously
promising results, concluded to apply for a regular
patent. For the purpose he sought the services of a
patent attorney in order to have his application pro-
fessionally drawn and filed. Acting as his own
patent solicitor, Berliner had invested only ten dollars for a *caveat*. He now engaged an attorney, one
James L. Norris, whose fees, Berliner thought,
would be within reach of his slender purse, to over-
see the drafting of an application for patent. The
young inventor was blissfully unconscious that he
was thrusting upon Norris a piece of electrical wizardry so utterly strange that even the most erudite
of patent lawyers of the time would hardly have
been equal to it. Nor did Berliner dream that one

day his ingenuousness would elicit from the eminent patent lawyers of the Bell Telephone Company the lamentation that he had not, as in the case of his *caveat,* drafted his own application for patent.

During the luncheon hour of a late May day in 1877, young Berliner hurried into Norris' law office, which occupied a small up-stairs room on Seventh Street opposite the Patent Office. By the window stood a man contemplatively immersed in the favorite male pastime of the era—tobacco-chewing. He was unshaven and generally unkempt, and in his eye there was a groggy squint. Berliner stated his errand.

"Coombs," said lawyer Norris to the unprepossessing person at the window, who turned out to be a "scrivener" and, as Berliner observed, a marksman of no mean talent on the tobacco-spitting range, "take down this young man's ideas and write them into a patent specification."

Charles L. Coombs, the scrivener, as the patent litigation later was to bring out, received from Norris two dollars apiece for drawing up patent specifications. After two half-hour lunch periods spent with Berliner, Coombs evolved the microphone specification. It was, of course, before the time of typewriters. Next day Berliner received a flimsy letter-press tissue-paper copy of Coombs' professional masterpiece in the form of a specification, written by hand in ink. In spots the copy was almost illegible.

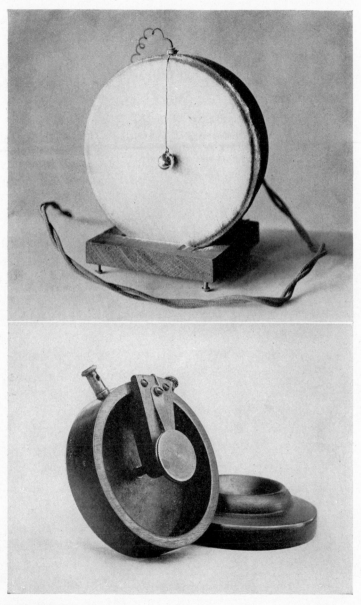

MICROPHONE OF MARCH 4, 1877. USED IN LAWSUITS IN 1879
STILL TRANSMITTING TODAY THE TICKING OF A WATCH AND EVERY
OTHER SOUND

MICROPHONE OF BERLINER'S CAVEAT, APRIL 14, 1877, WITH MOUTH-
PIECE ADDED

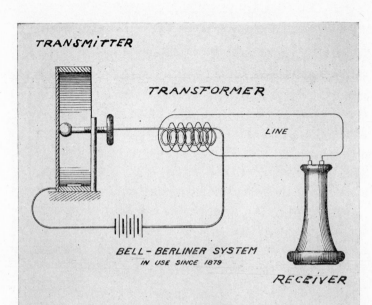

TRANSMITTER

TRANSFORMER

LINE

RECEIVER

BELL - BERLINER SYSTEM

IN USE SINCE 1879

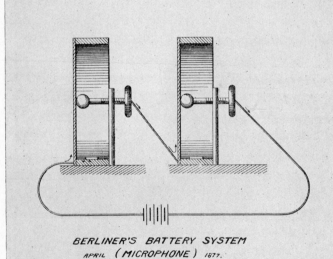

BERLINER'S BATTERY SYSTEM

APRIL (MICROPHONE) 1877.

Berliner had difficulty in deciphering Coombs' draft, but eventually discovered that it contained a number of poorly expressed statements. Meantime the application had been duly filed in the Patent Office under date of June 4, 1877, and the only remedy was to introduce amendments correcting Coombs' text. Berliner lost no time in filing these corrections, in full accordance with the legal procedure provided for such cases. In later years the forces opposing the Berliner patent made these amendments, necessitated by Coombs' slovenly work, one of the major pretexts for assailing the validity of Berliner's rights. The fact was that by the time the Patent Office reached Berliner's application, it had been corrected in every essential detail.

Berliner's invention struck the skilled examiners in the Patent Office as so wholly novel that in a letter addressed to Norris, dated September 19, 1877, they expressed doubts that so simple an instrument as a plate and a screw in contact with it could act as a telephone receiving apparatus. Berliner thereupon invited the examiners to his lodgings and convinced them of the soundness of his invention.

Among the visitors who from time to time came to Berliner's room to observe his experiments and marvel at his achievements was A. S. Solomons, a prominent bookdealer. Mr. Solomons was a citizen of Washington of so eminent standing that he was selected as chairman of the joint committee of citizens and appointees of Congress to supervise memorial services in the House of Representatives in memory of Professor Morse, inventor of the telegraph. Mr. Solomons was apparently very much impressed with what Berliner showed him, and, before leaving, asked if the inventor would not like to be introduced to Professor Joseph Henry, who was an electrician of great distinction and had been at the head of the Smithsonian Institution for a generation. Professor Henry was the sympathizing confidant of inventors in scientific branches and a discriminating extinguisher of pretenders.

Berliner naturally expressed the greatest eagerness to meet Professor Henry, and about the middle of July, 1877, accompanied Mr. Solomons to the Smithsonian Institution for that purpose. The inventor of the microphone explained to Professor Henry what he had, and the latter revealed the liveliest interest in Berliner's story. He said that at any time Berliner had the instruments ready to show, he would be pleased to have them brought to the Smithsonian and inspect their workings. Berliner subsequently took them there and exhibited them. Professor Henry was fascinated and addressed encouraging words to Berliner.

On the second of October, 1877, there appeared in the *National Republican,* of Washington, D. C., the following short account of the episode:

"Yesterday afternoon there was a very interesting exhibition at the Smithsonian Institution before

Professor Henry of a number of discoveries and inventions of Mr. E. Berliner, of this city. The inventions consisted of improved apparatus and modes of electric communication. The first instrument exhibited was the 'contact telephone' for transmitting sound vibrations from plate to plate, so as to enable persons to communicate. The second was the 'electric spark telephone,' which produced the same result by another process, that of the transmission of a spark. The third instrument was a 'telephonic transfer,' designed for transmitting sound by changes in the intensity of the circuit.''

Berliner filed an application for patent of his invention of the continuous current transformer on October 16, 1877. A patent was issued to him on January 15, 1878. Within a comparatively few months now, Berliner's unaided struggles were about to come to an end. He had invented the speaking microphone and thus completed the telephone. His rights and theories were indisputable, though soon to be long and bitterly contested. And so we pass to the next phase of Emile Berliner's development—the realization of his aspiration to play an integral part in the practical exploitation of the telephone.

CHAPTER XII

THE year 1878 was to be the year of practical destiny for Emile Berliner in the field of telephony—the stage of transition from hopes, dreams and pioneer achievements to the realm of actual association with the industry. Having invented the microphone, which completed Bell's telephone, and patented the continuous current transformer, which still further improved it, Berliner set promptly about the business of reaping the material rewards of his trials and triumphs.

By this time commercial telephony had staggered into its swaddling clothes. Bell, the wizard, with his assistant, Watson, an enthusiastic mechanic, and his far-sighted backers, Hubbard, dreamer and builder of air castles, and Thomas Sanders, the moneyed man of the combination, organized in Boston the nucleus of the Bell System, and began to improve, manufacture and install a few magneto telephones, to be used between individual homes and offices. The idea of inter-connecting the isolated groups soon followed, and the first switchboard was a natural, though at that time a very crude, development.

Within a week of the granting of his transformer

102

patent, Berliner placed himself in communication with the lawyers of the Telephone Company of New York (a subsidiary of the Bell Company), Messrs. Dickerson and Beaman, with offices in the old New-Yorker Staats-Zeitung Building in City Hall Square. In these modern days of Brobdingnagian finance, when capitalists and corporations juggle with millions as an every-hour pastime, it is difficult to read without a smile the following result of Berliner's baptismal dip into the commercial waters of telephony:

"New York, Jan. 22, 1878.

"Emile Berliner, Esq.,
818 7th St., N. W., Washington, D. C.

"My dear Sir:

"Yours of Jan. 20 and 21 received. I do not suppose that you seriously believe that your invention is worth $12,000 at the present time. The entire stock of the Telephone Company of New York is only $20,000. So you see that your interest would make a large share of that company. However that may be, we think it worth while to communicate with you further in the matter.

"I am therefore authorized to say in behalf of the Telephone Company of New York that they will be glad to have you call upon them here, in relation to the sale of your matters in the Patent Office and to such other arrangements as may seem advisable; and they offer to pay your expenses during such visit to them here.

"Please answer whether or not it will be convenient for you to come and meet with the managers of the company in this matter. If so, as I before said, they will be responsible for your expenses.

"Yours truly,
"E. N. Dickerson."

Berliner, though as yet a callow novice in the tortuous field of business, returned an adroit reply, which lost nothing in directness because of its quaint English:

"Washington, D. C.,
"January 24, 1878.

"E. N. Dickerson Jr., Esq.,
"New York City.
"Dear Sir:

"Your favor of the 22nd inst. came to hand. I fail to see the correctness of your argument to make the value of an invention dependent upon the capital of a Stock Company.

"Still, aside from a present result of our negotiations, I believe that a meeting with the managers of the Telephone Company would only be promotive to general telephonic interests. Wherefore I beg to accept their very polite offer made through you and will call at your office at about 10 A. M. this coming Saturday.

"Yours very truly,
"E. Berliner."

Mr. Dickerson acknowledged Berliner's letter next day in a telegram over the wires of the "Atlantic and Pacific Telegraph Company," saying: "Glad to see you Saturday. Bring your instruments." Berliner went to New York, but negotiations with the Telephone Company came to naught. Hilborne L. Roosevelt and Charles A. Cheever, its managers, were interested in his apparatus, but not to the extent of desiring to acquire it. Yet the visit to the Telephone Company was by no means fruitless. It led directly to relations between Gardiner

G. Hubbard, Alexander Graham Bell's father-in-law
and first president of the Bell Telephone Company
at Boston—relations which were speedily to eventuate in the realization of Berliner's burning desire
to join the interests now bent upon exploiting telephony on the grand scale.

The founders of the Bell System had very little
money, but they had great faith. They were embarked upon a long and arduous struggle to establish a telephone service, and make it self-supporting,
while developing and improving the telephone itself,
interesting the public in its use and inducing
investors to provide means for its growth.

Every sort of an obstacle seemed to block their
progress. Bell's patents were attacked, formidable
competition appeared and technical difficulties which
seemed insurmountable had to be met. Emile Berliner, though blissfully ignorant of it at this stage
of his endeavors, was himself cast for the title rôle
in a drama of litigation destined to be almost endless.

Nevertheless, there came to the Bell group a
period of growth and expansion. By lectures and
demonstrations the telephone was brought to public
attention at home and abroad. A demand for instruments arose in many cities almost simultaneously, a demand greater than it was possible to
supply immediately. In spite of its constant struggle for existence, the Bell group adopted a policy
of progress and improvement, and it was in conse-

quence of that program that Berliner's ambition in the Bells' direction was ultimately to be gratified.

Berliner's first contact with the Bell interests was the result of a letter of introduction from the management of the Telephone Company of New York:

THE TELEPHONE COMPANY OF NEW YORK
32 Tribune Building
"New York, Jan. 26, 1878.
"Hon. G. G. Hubbard,
"Dear Sir:
"This will introduce to you Mr. E. Berliner who has a very interesting Telephone that I would like you to examine, as some of the principles are very curious and may be of much importance. He lives in Washington and will be pleased to show his apparatus.
"Very truly yours,
"Hilborne L. Roosevelt."

Two days later the Telephone Company wrote Berliner that Mr. Hubbard was now in New York and the Berliner apparatus would be explained to him there, so that he could examine it the more diligently when he went to Washington the following week. "You might send me two machines to try," Mr. Roosevelt added, "when you have them in good shape. Your experiments have interested me very much. I will be pleased to hear from you from time to time, and will notify you before I shall come to Washington. I will also report your offer in the matter of experiments."

This correspondence marks the real inauguration of Berliner's association with the purely commercial side of telephony. Thenceforward there was an uninterrupted exchange of letters between the inventor and the men who were on the threshold of becoming the telephone magnates of America. The latter undertook forthwith to examine Berliner's apparatus and his patents, with a view to their acquisition if they turned out to be as promising as they seemed. As for Berliner, he devoted himself assiduously during the spring of 1878 to perfecting, through ceaseless experiment, the principles and mechanism he had already worked out.

Meantime, ominous clouds were gathering in the United States Patent Office. These clouds, which do not always develop a silver lining, are technically known as "interferences." When several inventors come into the Patent Office with applications for patents that apply to the same or similar inventions, the applications are "stopped" by the examiners and referred to a bureau which formally declares what patent law terms an "interference." Thereupon, every rival inventor is required to file a statement detailing just when he conceived his own invention and when it was put into practise. The next step is a complicated and protracted legal inquiry, which may last for months, or even years. Eventually the inventor deemed worthy of priority rights obtains his patent.

During 1877 and early in 1878 other inventors

than Berliner filed at the Patent Office their applications for transmitter patents. Thus it came about that on March 16, 1878, an extensive "interference" was declared by the Commissioner of Patents.

The Bell Telephone Company was keeping an eagle eye upon all developments in the telephone field, particularly in the domain of patents. At the end of the spring of 1878 the Bell interests were represented at Washington by Gardiner G. Hubbard, as trustee. The Bell telephone at this stage was much talked about, but little believed in. Practically no outsider was willing to venture the investment of capital in it. The idea of conversation over telegraph wires continued to be regarded as a chimera. Hubbard's job in Washington was mainly to "sell" the practicability of the telephone to anybody who would stand still long enough to listen to his persuasive "drummer's" story of its miraculous possibilities. A stately, gray-bearded, confidence-inspiring figure, Hubbard seldom failed to carry conviction. He trundled his pair of Bell telephones around Washington tirelessly, seeking opportunities to show them to the most prominent men he could approach. One of these was Theodore N. Vail, the virile young superintendent of the United States Railway Mail Service.

Presently the Bell group had its attention called to the possible development of a transmitter operated by a battery. Forthwith they wrote their Washington attorney, an exceptionally shrewd lawyer named Anthony Pollok, to investigate the "interference" declared by the Patent Office and find out whether there were any transmitter patents on file which the Bell interests ought to acquire or control. Pollok made an exhaustive survey of the situation and reported to the Bell Telephone Company that the only application which, in his judgment, was worthy of their interest was the one filed by Emile Berliner on June 4, 1877, covering the loose contact transmitter.

Four names at this time stood out in the "interference" cases before the Patent Office. They were Professor Alexander Graham Bell, scientifically educated and with interested and influential men at his back; Professor Elisha Gray, of Chicago, a learned scientist of middle age; Professor Amos E. Dolbear, of Tufts College; and Thomas A. Edison, already a well-known and recognized inventor in the field of telegraphy. Such was the galaxy of technical talent and financial strength against which Emile Berliner—be it remembered, still a "counter-jumper" in an inconspicuous store in Washington—confronted in the struggle for recognition of his rights in the United States Patent Office.

It was in the midst of his uninterrupted experiments at his rooming-house "laboratory" on Sixth Street, Washington, that Berliner about this time struck up an acquaintance with the young woman who was destined to become, and still is, his life partner. Now and then, Berliner would stretch a line across the street from his lodgings to the home of friendly neighbors named Adler. Eventually he met the two attractive daughters of the house, one of whom he proceeded to woo and win. It was pioneering in telephony that resulted in Alexander Graham Bell and the daughter of Gardiner G. Hubbard becoming man and wife. Now, the same sort of tinkering with talk transmission was to lead to the altar Emile Berliner and Cora Adler.

One day a messenger boy electrified the clerical staff at the Behrend store on Seventh Street by asking for Emile Berliner and announcing that the latter's presence was desired at the office of Anthony Pollok. Pollok's name was widely known in Washington. A summons to his legal throne was a badge of distinction. Berliner's fellow-clerks were correspondingly impressed. Pollok, like Berliner, was European-born. The inventor found the lawyer to be a man of swarthy complexion, keen-eyed and adorned with a goatee affected by Frenchmen of the era. Pollok talked with directness and decision.

"The Bell Telephone Company," he said, going straight to the point of the interview, "is interested in your invention. Thomas A. Watson, the superintendent of the company, would like to come here and see your apparatus."

Berliner was naturally elated over this prima facie evidence that he was at last within sight of his cherished goal—a close scientific identification with the interests which were converting the telephone from a crudity, the ultimate possibilities of which were not yet faintly imagined, into a public utility. It was always as a *scientist* that Berliner longed for recognition in the field in which he now was an acknowledged pioneer. Amid such emotions and secret anticipations he awaited the approaching interview with Watson—the man to whom Bell had transmitted the first complete and coherent message ever telephoned.

The superintendent of the Bell Company came to Washington. It was a tall, energetic, intensely practical-looking New Englander who swung open the front door of the Behrend store one dull rainy day and proclaimed that he had business there with a young person named Emile Berliner. The idling clerks, "mute, inglorious" like all clerks in humble shops since time immemorial, were visibly awed, for it was an unusual happening on humdrum Seventh Street. The boss gave Berliner time off to "tinker" with his "toys" in his lodgings around the corner, as soon as the inventor-clerk disclosed the eminent identity of his visitor. Berliner led Watson around to the little room on Sixth Street, showed him pridefully the magic soap-box, and then the pair clattered down the two flights of stairs and out to the barn in the rear of the house, to which Berliner's "telephone line" ran.

No other man at that time, unless it was Alexander Graham Bell himself, was so familiar with the art of electrical acoustics, and therefore so well able to recognize new merit in that realm, as Thomas A. Watson. With his own hands he had shaped the original Bell mechanism. He knew what the Bell telephone would do. Also, he knew what it would not do. While Berliner's apparatus was almost the crudest thing imaginable, Watson was prepared, by the process of elimination, to see at once that here was a logical and an entirely novel way of sending voice undulations by wire. The Bell telephone "wafted" them. But in this new contrivance, after being most minutely and perfectly caught, they were *sent*, and the power that sent them could even be automatically "stepped up." Realizing that he was inspecting a telephone system that ignored Bell's mechanical contrivance entirely, Watson, in far-sighted vision, pondered thoughtfully what this thing might lead to. After a brief twenty minutes, he concluded his visit with the impressive words, *"We will want that, Mr. Berliner. You will hear from us in a few days."*

Watson, returning from Washington, seemed convinced that the Bells' hope lay in young Berliner. His instrument was unique; he was the originator of the continuous current transformer, the only one directly applicable to the telephone; he already possessed the patent for this (which idea was also being usurped and utilized by the Bells' menacing and aggressive rivals, the Western Union); and in Berliner's eye Watson detected the glint of genius. During the next few weeks a flow of correspondence came to Berliner from Watson, Vail and Hubbard, paving the way for his eventual connection with the Bell interests.

In June, 1878, Berliner submitted to the Bell Telephone Company through Gardiner G. Hubbard at Washington an offer which provoked from the latter the following reply:

"Dear Sir:

"I received your note two days ago. Your proposition seems to be fair excepting in regard to the time you allow for accepting it. I could not conclude to accept it until I see Mr. Watson, who is at Chicago.

"If you will extend the time and make it six weeks, I think we can make an arrangement with you. Until after Congress adjourns, I can not agree to attend to any new business. Will you please bring your new telephones to my room? I should like to try them with you."

The Bell interests had now engaged as their general manager the man who was destined to be of profound influence, during the ensuing generation, upon telephone and telegraph development. He was that masterful "high voltage" personality, *bon vivant,* and born organizer, Theodore N. Vail, the superintendent of the United States Railway Mail Service, whose interest in the telephone was first aroused by Gardiner G. Hubbard. Vail, now headquartered in New York, was almost Heaven-sent for the Bell group's purposes. He had moved with such celerity on behalf of his new associates that within

a few weeks his forceful and magnetic methods resulted in reorganizing their company with genuine
capital of four hundred and fifty thousand dollars—
a mint of money for a new enterprise in those days.

On July 2, 1878, Vail wrote Emile Berliner as
follows:

"I intended to see you when in Washington
lately in regard to your letter to Mr. Hubbard con-
cerning your improvements in telephony.

"I wish you would continue your proposition,
so as to cover the month of July. During this month
we can come to some understanding, which will be
to our mutual advantage. I am speaking now as
general manager of the Bell Telephone Company.

"By that time we will have settled our headquarters in New York, and arranged matters now
pending that will influence to a certain extent any
arrangement we can make with you as to your entering the service of the Company, etc. We have about
made arrangements with a company manufacturing telephone instruments here, for facilities to experiment, etc.

"I shall be in Washington by the 16th and will
see you after my arrival. Please write me whether
you will consent to this extension of time, etc."

A week after receipt of Vail's letter, Berliner
heard from Thomas A. Watson, superintendent of
the Bell Telephone at Boston, enclosing a money
order for four dollars and fifty cents, covering the
cost of certain legal papers, and adding:

"Our Company is being reorganized and the ex-
ecutive offices will probably be transferred to New
York. When that is done, I think some arrange-

ment will be made with you by which you can enter our service.''

On July 17, 1878, true to his pledge, Vail, writing Berliner from the Post Office Department in Washington, said:

"What time to-day could I see you for a few moments in relation to telephone matters? If you could make it convenient to step in my office, I would not detain you long, and think we could settle on some terms.''

Matters now were moving so rapidly in the negotiations between Berliner and the Bell people—Vail, Hubbard and Watson—that the coveted contract providing for Berliner's entering the Bell company's employment was imminent. Bell headquarters was now at 66 and 68 Reade Street, New York. On September 7, 1878, Berliner heard from Hubbard at New York in these terms:

"Mr. Vail returned last night sick, so I have not seen him. He sent me a line saying you would be here on Monday with full copies of your specifications. I have written Mr. Watson to come on from Boston, to meet you at that time. So if you can not come, telegraph what day you will be here. It is, however, important that we lose no time.''

It was about at this time that the Western Union, with its net of wires spreading across the country and its unlimited capital, had decided to enter the telephone field. To that end it had begun to put out imitation receivers and a battery transmitter devised by Thomas A. Edison.

"Give us a good transmitter!" became the cry of the Bell Company's eager managers, now almost frantic in their efforts to be first in the telephone field and thwart the Western Union's bold bid for supremacy. The Bells wanted Berliner's ideas, and they wanted *him*. They were rapidly whipping their affairs into shape under Vail's energetic generalship and, once possessed of a good transmitter, were confident of beating back the Western Union's attack.

Vail was in Washington occasionally during the ensuing weeks and met Berliner by appointment. The two men came cordially to like each other. Vail's faith in Berliner and in what he could do for the telephone gained fresh impetus when he learned that a *caveat,* a supposedly secret paper fully describing the microphone, had been deposited by Berliner in the Patent Office as early as April 14, 1877. Vail was impressed too, by the fact that this young inventor possessed enough business acumen not to disclose the secrets of this document, even under tempting circumstances, until he had actually signed a contract with the company. Here was manifestly not the average "impractical inventor." Vail discerned, on the contrary, a mentality of unusual symmetry.

How to make a satisfactory agreement on the basis of nothing but a prospective patent already blocked in an "interference" was the difficulty that existed when Berliner talked "business" with Vail.

It showed conclusively that the Bell Company, after carefully studying the situation, not only concluded that Berliner's conception of a battery transmitter was scientifically correct, but that he had a first-class chance to prevail in the Patent Office. David Edward Hughes, in England, had only a short time before sustained the Berliner idea in his experiments with loose contacts. All this, and the transformer patent which Berliner already possessed, made the latter entirely too valuable a man for the Bells to lose.

Hence, by September they made Berliner the kind of offer that appealed to him. Unknown to his friends or employer, a two-day trip which he made to New York that month was for the express purpose of signing an agreement with the Bell Company. It provided for a moderate salary and a royalty on export transmitters. All that Berliner was able to turn over to the Company was the control of his *caveats*, and his patent applications that were still pending in the Patent Office, as well as the use of his induction coil, or transformer, patent. Several years afterward the Bell Company paid Berliner a lump sum and largely increased his annual retainer, which took the place of salary, because he later left Boston and went to work for himself.

CHAPTER XIII

BERLINER COMPLETES THE TELEPHONE

THROUGHOUT his seven American years of stress, struggle and final success, Emile Berliner had never known a day of illness worthy of the name. But now the cumulative effect of physical and mental strain was to exact inevitable toll from him.

Behind the young inventor lay eighteen months of tremendous effort. He had experimented ceaselessly and intensively with his telephone apparatus. He had, virtually unaided, taken the first hurdles at the United States Patent Office. He had weathered a maiden experience with "Big Business." Always a conscientious purveyor of gents' furnishings and bookkeeper at the Behrend store, he had burned the candle at both ends, employing each and every moment off duty in tinkering and toying with the mechanism so soon destined to revolutionize human intercourse.

The word play found no place in Emile Berliner's lexicon. His absorption in things scientific was complete. It found constant expression in letters to his kith and kin in Germany. Once a brother in Hanover wrote sternly to admonish

118

Emile against pursuing the elusive shadow of telephony at the expense of the tangible substance of dry goods, which was affording him an honest living!

Almost immediately after the realization of his supreme ambition in associating himself with the Bell interests in September, 1878, Berliner suffered a breakdown. Nerves ordinarily taut now tired and relaxed. Then came exhaustion, and, finally, collapse. Berliner was just back from his conclusive visit with the Bell group in New York when he fainted in his lodgings at Washington. A wearisome period of illness ensued.

He was now to pay the price of his long vigil of strangeness and loneliness in a new land. He had never known in America the caressing influence of a home environment, nor the stimulus that is born of intimate relationships with confident friends. In the Behrend store, surrounded by sordid indifference toward the higher things which were engaging his thought, the inventor was perforce compelled to conceal his hopes, to suppress his dreams and generally to erase his real self in order that it might fit into the workaday scheme within which bread-and-butter requirements pinioned him. It was those psychological conditions, as much as actual wear and tear in a physical sense, that sentenced Emile Berliner to an enforced period of inactivity and correspondingly irksome sojourn in a sickbed. Through the window of his room in Providence Hospital he could glimpse the glittering white dome of the Capitol, and he derived fresh hope and determination from that inspiring symbol of the land of opportunity.

For six weeks he was a patient at Providence. News of Berliner's contract with the Bell interests had spread through the scientific world at Washington and among Berliner's narrow circle of friends. Among the first to congratulate him was Mr. Solomons, the book dealer who, the year previous, had brought Berliner and his work to the attention of Professor Joseph Henry, at the Smithsonian Institution. "It affords me sincere pleasure to learn," wrote Mr. Solomons, "that your merits as an inventor have at last been recognized in a substantial manner, and I can assure you it will always be gratifying to me to hear of your continued success."

The daughters of the Solomons house, who are to-day among the distinguished women of Washington, perpetuate the family friendship with Emile Berliner, who looks upon their father as one of his earliest benefactors.

From his new associates of the Bell Telephone Company, words of encouragement were not lacking, either. "I am very sorry to hear of your sickness," wrote Gardiner G. Hubbard, from New York, on October 1, 1878, "and trust it will not be of long continuance."

Theodore N. Vail, General Manager of the Bell

Telephone Company, was one of Berliner's periodical visitors at Providence Hospital. That visible evidence of the Bell Company's interest in their new collaborator was as medicine and fresh air to the prostrate inventor. Buoyant, optimistic, dynamic, Vail was an unfailing tonic. His bedside calls, invariably marked by encouraging prophecies of Berliner's future in the telephone field, acted like electric energy poured into a run-down battery: Vail's visits helped materially to fortify the patient against the depressing dictum of physicians that Berliner should not resume work for a whole year. That advice had all the annihilating effect of a prison sentence on the eager young scientist, now longing more impatiently than ever to travel the path of opportunity that at last was opened to him.

Since those formative days, forty-eight years ago, Emile Berliner has had one or two other nervous breakdowns. Yet, past seventy-five, he contends that his nerve structure is more rugged than at any previous time in his life. When asked how he overcame his first collapse and by the same methods triumphed over later ones, Berliner clenches his fists, grits his teeth, snaps into a setting-up posture, and says: "Just like this—by holding on!—and by a firm confidence that proper rest always effects eventual cure."

Berliner's theory, time-tried and experience-tested, is that nervous breakdowns as such are purely physiological. "Under a continuous strain," he explains, "the sheathing of the nerve fibers becomes sore and more or less inflamed. In that condition they affect the brain and give rise to morbid, pessimistic and even suicidal thoughts. If one will only be patient and give the system a chance to pull itself together under more favorable conditions, nerves will become as strong again as they were before collapse."

The solicitude of Gardiner G. Hubbard and Theodore N. Vail for the speedy recovery of Emile Berliner was born of something more than genuinely sympathetic and sincere interest in his health. In the letter expressing hope that he would soon be up and about, Hubbard had written: "Mr. Watson's view is that we should take immediate steps for having your invention patented in Great Britain and Canada, and I will prepare and forward the necessary papers for you to sign in a day or two."

Unbeknown to Berliner himself, he had become an almost indispensable factor in the Bell Telephone Company's calculations. Indeed, what he had invented, and that which the Bells acquired from him—the control of Berliner's *caveats* and patent applications, as well as the use of his induction coil patent—*seemed to be the rocks to which the whole Bell enterprise was about to cling for security and for the realization of its uncharted future.*

After Alexander Graham Bell had obtained the patent for his telephone invention, he and Watson continued to improve it, until they reached a point at which they thought it could be sold to the Western Union Telegraph Company. The Bell patent rights were offered to the Western Union for one hundred thousand dollars, which was "real money" half a century ago. That already great corporation was the logical agency for turning the telephone to practical purposes. But the management of the Western Union (later headed by Theodore N. Vail) was not so astute or far-seeing as its successors, and it rejected the Bell-Watson proposition. It did not want the Bell telephone—that is to say, it did not covet the prize as yet.

Later, when the patent's immeasurable possibilities were grasped, the Western Union of that day simply decided to annex it more or less by main force. Millions of capital and shrewd captains of finance stood behind the company. It did not seriously occur to the Western Union high command that a little thing like Bell's patent—"a mere scrap of paper"—could impede the progress of the colossus that now occupied, almost unchallenged, the field of electrical communication. The Bell Company's position seemed all the more contemptible and defenseless, from the standpoint of the Western Union, in view of its financial weakness. "The giant expected to crush the pigmy with a blow," records Albert Bigelow Paine in his biography of Theodore N. Vail (*In One Man's Life*). "The popularity of the telephone grew amazingly," writes Paine, "and the demand for instruments increased beyond the limits of the Bell Company to manufacture, and especially beyond its ability to purchase. The company was constantly on the verge of bankruptcy, through its prosperity."

But in addition to its slender capital resources, the Bell Company seemed vulnerable, in the Western Union's eyes, because of the technical impression the Bell telephone itself made. It was very remote from perfection. One still required to shout into it, and often to repeat the shouts several times, to be heard or understood. The magneto transmitter in particular was so primitive—more designed, as Watson himself admitted on a later occasion, "to develop the American voice and lungs than to promote conversation." The thing seemed indeed so utterly crude that the Western Union persuaded itself it would not have to face a serious competitor for some time to come. So for its technical purpose, the company leagued three of the best-known electrical inventors of the day—Thomas A. Edison, Elisha Gray and Amos E. Dolbear—and, under the name of the American Speaking Telephone Company, proceeded to drive at full speed into the field of telephony. With a bluster destined to cost it dearly a few years later, the company proclaimed that it possessed "the only original telephone," flouting Bell's rights as if they had never existed. "The fact that all three of its inventors, Edison, Gray and Dolbear, had each and severally fully acknowledged Bell's rights apparently was little regarded, especially as Gray and Dolbear were now quite willing to repudiate such acknowledgments and assert prior claims."*

By a singular coincidence, Edison's patent application for a flat disk transmitter was filed at the United States Patent Office in Washington *just thirteen days after* Berliner deposited there his *caveat* for the microphone. Mr. Edison for some years had maintained his own well-equipped laboratories and was now fully prepared to aid and abet the Western Union in its raid for priority. It should be observed, in passing, that the Western Union Telegraph Company of 1926 is a wholly different enterprise, in respect of policy, personnel and management, from the organization which so adventurously embarked upon the uncharted sea of telephony in 1879.

"Lessees of Bell telephones," writes Herbert N. Casson (*History of the Telephone*), "clamored with one voice for a transmitter as good as Edison's. This, of course, could not be had in a moment, and the five months that followed were the darkest days in the childhood of the telephone. How to compete with the Western Union, which had this superior transmitter, a host of agents, a network of wires, forty million dollars of capital, and a first claim upon all newspapers, hotels, railroads, and rights of way—that was the immediate problem that confronted Theodore N. Vail, the Bell's new general

---

In One Man's Life, page 102.

manager. Several of his captains deserted, and he was compelled to take control of their unprofitable exchanges. There was scarcely a mail that did not bring him some bulletin of discouragement or defeat.''

But the ''Big Four'' now in charge of Bell fortunes—Bell himself, Watson, Hubbard and Vail—had no notion of giving up the ship. On the contrary, the Liliputians determined to strike the Western Union a blow that would go straight to the vitals of the onrushing Gulliver. To that end they put a discerning finger on the pulse of their distressful situation—they must secure a transmitter that would *outclass* the lampblack transmitter developed by Edison, which was now in so serious danger of making the Western Union's telephone apparatus more popular than Bell's mechanism. The public, it was realized, cared nothing about patent rights. What it wanted was telephone service. It was ready to subscribe for the most efficient instruments it could get, no matter whence they came.

It was in the midst of this threatened submergence by the Western Union avalanche that Emile Berliner came within the Bell Telephone Company's orbit with all the providential effectiveness of a lifesaver. Then and thus it was that Watson, at Vail's instigation, had sought out Berliner in Washington, consequential upon the initial interview with Pollok, the patent lawyer; had inspected the inventor's little soap-box microphone and spoken those

(Form 106.)

The Telephone Company of New York,

32 TRIBUNE BUILDING,

HILBORNE L. ROOSEVELT,
CHARLES A. CHEEVER, } Managers   New York, Jan 26 1878

Hon. G. G. Hubbard —

Dear Sir,

This will introduce to you Mr. E. Berliner who has a very interesting Telephone that I would like you to examine as some of the principals are very curious and may be of much importance. He lives in Washington & will be pleased to show you his apparatus.

Very truly Yours

Hilborne L. Roosevelt

LETTER FROM TELEPHONE COMPANY OF NEW YORK INTRODUCING
EMILE BERLINER TO THE BELL GROUP

LETTER FROM MR. HUBBARD   GARDINER GREENE HUBBARD IN 1876

words—prophetic for Berliner and, as time was to show, of literally vital importance to the Bells: *"Young man, we will want that, You will hear from us in a few days."*

Six weeks elapsed between the consummation of Berliner's agreement with the Bell interests, followed by his breakdown in Washington, and the commencement of his service under the employment contract. In November, 1878, against the urgent advice of his physician, he proceeded to New York for that purpose. The Bell Telephone Company's headquarters at 66 and 68 Reade Street occupied only half of a second floor. The equipment was of Spartan simplicity, consisting all told of two or three plain deal desks and chairs—the forerunner of the marble pile that is now at 195 Broadway.

In that modest environment—the cradle of the mighty "Bell System" of this day—Theodore N. Vail was organizing the affairs of the company with steam-engine zeal. He had only one assistant—a certain R. W. Devonshire—who sent out in longhand all of the correspondence. Typewriters had not yet emerged. Emile Berliner's accomplishments, dating from schooldays in Hanover, included uncommon skill in Spencerian penmanship, of which, at seventy-five, he is still a master, so Vail, for the time being, commandeered his services as a general utility man in the Bell offices.

It was about this time that Francis Blake, of Boston, a scientist formerly attached to the United

States Geodetic Survey at Washington, designed an ingenious modification of the Berliner loose contact microphone. He had been working on it at the Williams electrical shop in Boston in an effort to put it into practical condition, and eventually sold it to the Bell Company. Figuring out microphonic action was a deep and intricate problem—one that took about all the strength and ingenuity a man possessed, for it was at this stage of his experiments that Francis Blake, like Berliner a little while before, was prostrated by a nervous breakdown, with his work unfinished.

The value of the Blake transmitter modification lay in an ingenious suspension, on two flat springs, of a hard carbon button and a bead of platinum in such a way that the two would not easily separate when vibrated by the diaphragm against which they leaned. When carefully adjusted and addressed by a trained speaker the Blake transmitter would work very well. But it took practise to talk into it, and, if adjusted in the evening, it might be entirely out of adjustment the next morning. Of course, such an instrument was entirely unfit to be placed in commission. It was at this precise period that Berliner's important and *practical* work for the Bell Company commenced.

As the days sped by and the Western Union challenge remained unmet, the Bell agents became more and more insistent upon securing a good battery transmitter because whenever the Western Union

Company came to prospective subscribers for telephone service with lampblack transmitters, these proved superior to the Bell magneto transmitter. The situation, already acute, now threatened to become critical. At the end of January, 1879, Vail and Watson decided to send Berliner to Boston, to take up his experimental duties at the company's laboratory in the Williams shop and finish Blake's work while the latter was sick abed. In the *incredibly brief period of six weeks* Berliner perfected the Blake transmitter, so that two hundred instruments could be made in a day, and, once adjusted, would remain so indefinitely.

The American Telephone and Telegraph Company of this day retains in its archives an account written by Emile Berliner narrating in detail what had to be done in order to save the ingenious Blake form of transmitter from being a pronounced failure. The account is of so historic importance in the development of telephony, and of so absorbing interest to all students of electrical apparatus, who nowadays include "radio fans," that it has been deemed worthy of reproduction as an appendix to this volume. (See page 314.) It shows what keen and exact reasoning a successful inventor must apply in order to accomplish his purposes. Incidentally, it visualizes the condition into which the budding art of telephony had fallen.

"The status of the Blake transmitter, when I took hold of it," wrote Emile Berliner, "was, briefly, that it was not possible to make twelve transmitters alike good, and when these were adjusted at night, they were out of adjustment the next morning." Berliner's plodding efforts eventually detected the flaws in the Blake mechanism. As soon as Berliner reported that it had been perfected, orders were given that two hundred a day should be made. Berliner himself, with his assistant, Richards, tested each of them minutely. Once adjusted, they remained in first-class working order. Berliner personally inspected and tested the first twenty thousand transmitters for the Bell Company. Then that branch of the business was turned over to Richards. Thereafter the inventor devoted himself to research work for the Bell Company and assisted Professor Charles R. Cross, of the Massachusetts Institute of Technology, in the exhaustive experiments which the latter conducted for James J. Storrow in support of that patent lawyer's astute defense of the Bell-Berliner patents and of his unceasing attack upon infringers.

The Blake transmitter as perfected by Berliner was vastly superior to the Edison lampblack transmitter, which was being put out by the rival telephone concern, the Gold and Stock Telegraph Company, for use of subscribers. This was a subsidiary of the Western Union, specially organized and operated for the benefit of stock-brokerage houses which had their own telegraph operators. Momentous events in the telephone world were now brewing.

They were to demonstrate that Berliner's work saved the day for the Bell Company, though not until after the contenders for supremacy in the telephone field had fought a long and costly duel in the arena of the highest courts of the republic.

Nearly all of us whose memory runs back to the earliest telephones in general use will recall that Berliner's name appeared prominently on the Blake transmitter affixed to the wooden box telephones of that ancient era. The author remembers vividly the first telephones installed in his native La Porte, Indiana, that "Maple City" which nestles so picturesquely in the northwestern Hoosier county lapped by the waters of Lake Michigan. He recalls the invincible skepticism of an eighty-year-old La Porte grandmother, who had never learned to speak English. A grandson, of whom she was especially fond, had learned German to please her. Because he was attorney for the local Bell Company, some of the first instruments installed in La Porte were placed in his office and her home. The young lawyer's opening conversation was held with his grandmother in her language. The astonished and somewhat affrighted octogenarian remarked later in the day, after recovering her equilibrium, that she didn't think it a particularly wonderful thing that *Amerikaner* should have invented something enabling *English* to be talked by wire. But that they had discovered a device whereby *German* could be spoken by telephone—*that,* the

old lady insisted, was positively the last word in the
way of a scientific marvel—*Kolossal!*

The author, many years afterward long sta-
tioned in Berlin as a newspaper correspondent, seldom said *Wer dort?* (Who's there?—the German
equivalent for Hello) over the Kaiser's telephone
lines without recalling with a smile the La Porte
grandmother's quaint tribute to what Bell and Berliner between them had wrought.

CHAPTER XIV

THE TELEPHONE FIGHTS FOR ITS LIFE

BERLINER'S completion of the telephone placed the Bell Company in an extremely strong position not only by virtue of Bell's own broad patents, but also because the company now possessed incomparably the best instruments of the day. But as triumph is ever the mother of contention, the Bells speedily found themselves ambushed on all sides. They were on the threshold of attack, intrigue and rivalry that were to eventuate in lawsuits literally by the hundred, and to cost them in defensive measures more than a million of money and more than a decade of precious time. Before their herculean struggle for self-preservation was to end, they were to combat none other than the government of the United States of America itself.

The Bell telephone, of which the Berliner transmitter had now become a vitally integral part, was, in short, face to face with a fight for its life. No stone of recourse or of resource available to capital, legal acumen or human unscrupulousness was to be left unturned, to accomplish the ruin, first, of Bell, the inventor, and, then, of Berliner, the perfecter of the telephone.

The illimitable commercial possibilities of the new art were no longer in doubt. To "get rich quick" out of them, by hook or by crook, became the obsessing passion alike of recognized captains of industry and of piratical adventurers.

Telephony accordingly ushered in one of those "booms" which, in recurring cycles, fever the imaginations of the American people. Once it was gold that set men crazy; then, silver; in a more modern time, oil; latterly, Florida land. In the early 'eighties it was telephony. All over the country men were suddenly fired with the notion that Bell and Berliner had opened up a field that could be fabulously exploited by any one with a smattering of mechanical ingenuity and the enterprise to launch a wildcat stock-jobbing campaign.

To the more ruthless, the new field even held out the inviting possibilities of successful blackmail. In one form or another, the Bell group soon found itself called upon to baffle a long conspiracy of malice, envy and greed without parallel in business and legal history, measured in terms of the rich prize at stake and the duration of the contest. No fewer than six hundred defensive lawsuits were fought up to May 10, 1897, when the United States Supreme Court finally placed its historic hallmark, for all time, upon the validity of the Bell-Berliner patents and pronounced them unassailable.

Athwart the Bell's path lay primarily the Western Union Telegraph Company. Through its subsidiary, the Gold and Stock Telegraph Company, the Western Union had boldly invaded the telephone field. It commanded eminent engineering talent— Edison, Gray and Dolbear; owned a far-flung network of wires (all overhead in those days), and was ready to link the whole country into a system of telephone "central" stations and subscribers. Its next objective was to crush the only serious competitor in sight, the Bell Telephone Company. As an ally in that campaign, the Western Union found ready to hand the budding "granger movement" in the rural West, with its insensate hatred and fear of anything savoring of a "monopoly." So the Western Union interests of that day moved Heaven and earth to turn the anti-monopoly guns to its own uses and against the Bell Telephone Company. Congress and the press were ruthlessly exploited for the purpose.

The Western Union first trotted out Elisha Gray as the Simon-pure inventor of the telephone and forthwith began infringement proceedings against the Bell Company. The palpable purpose was to terrify the Bell group into a tame submission. The case began in the fall of 1878 and ended dramatically a year later on the advice of George Gifford, the Western Union's chief counsel, who notified his clients, point-blank, that Alexander Graham Bell was the unchallengeable inventor of the telephone. He advised them to sue for peace on the best terms the Bells would grant.

Months of conference finally resulted in a give-and-take arrangement. The Western Union agreed, under a covenant to run for seventeen years:

(1) To acknowledge Bell as the original inventor of the telephone.

(2) To concede that his patents were unassailable.

(3) To quit the telephone field.

On their part, the Bells agreed:

(1) To purchase the Western Union telephone system.

(2) To grant the Western Union twenty per cent. royalty on all rentals of telephones.

(3) To stay out of the telegraph field.

The Western Union having met its Waterloo, the Bell system came definitely and formally into its own as the standard, recognized and indisputable telephone organization of the country. Its stock sky-rocketed to one thousand dollars a share. Theodore N. Vail, the generalissimo of the whole triumphant crusade, reorganized the company, and in 1882, within three years of the victory over the Western Union, Bell Telephone gross earnings exceeded one million dollars. But the company's trials, especially its legal tribulations, were far from over. Once again Elisha Gray thrust himself into the picture. Not content to accept the defeat administered to the Western Union in 1879, he reasserted his claim to be the original inventor of the telephone.

The paths of Alexander Graham Bell and Elisha Gray had been running close together and in almost parallel lines for nearly ten years. In 1874 they were both engaged in a contest to invent the first harmonic telegraph. Gray held to that as his objective. But Bell turned to telephony. Yet each had always at the back of his head the notion of sending speech by wire. Thereupon ensued, as one of the freaks of Patent Office history, an amazing coincidence. Bell and Gray, utterly unbeknown to each other, selected the same day, on which to file, respectively, an application for a patent and a *caveat* on the identical subject. It was St. Valentine's Day—a stormy Monday, the fourteenth of February, 1876. Bell reached the Patent Office first, according to the book of record, in which as ''Cash Entry No. 5'' stood the legend: ''A. G. Bell, $15.'' Entry No. 39 read: ''E. Gray, $10.''

There was thus not only the documentary record of Bell's chronological priority, but an even more vital difference in the fact that Bell filed an application for a *patent,* while Gray had submitted only a *caveat.* When a man files an *application* for a patent, he declares that he has completed the invention. Gray's lawsuits were all unsuccessful. He was rebuffed at every turn.

Following Gray, as challenger of the Bell patents, came Professor Amos E. Dolbear, of Tufts College. Dolbear contended that he had ''improved'' the telephonic device originated by the

German, Philip Reis, of Frankfort, in 1861. But
Dolbear's claims, like Elisha Gray's, were not upheld. The famous court decision which rejected
them observed: "To follow Reis is to fail; but to
follow Bell is to succeed." It was testified during
the suit that Dolbear's telephone "would squeak, but
not speak."

Even with the scalps of the Western Union, Gray
and Dolbear dangling at its belt, the Bell Telephone
Company was to have no immunity from attack.
Telephony was making fortunes overnight forty
years ago, as oil and Florida land have created
millionaires in our day. That was why the Bells
were to know no peace at the hands of financial adventurers, shyster lawyers and fake inventors.

There now bounded into the arena of coveted
booty one Daniel Drawbaugh, resident of a Pennsylvania country town, whose yokel origin at first
aroused only the contempt of the Bell lawyers. But
Drawbaugh persisted with his claim to have invented
and used a telephone several years prior to its invention by Alexander Graham Bell. Dangling before
their eyes the prospects of millions in tribute to be
extorted from the Bell Company if he could establish
his pretensions, Drawbaugh induced a group of
Washington bankers to form the "People's Telephone Company." He persuaded these credulous
angels to finance, at vast cost to themselves, litigation that dragged through several years. But once
again the colors of the Bell System emerged vic-

torious. Drawbaugh turned out to be a village
tinker, with a weird mania for patterning the latest
kink in mechanics and grandiloquently claiming the
result as an earlier creation of his own. The decision throwing Drawbaugh's case out of court
censured him for "deliberately falsifying the
facts."

The Bell group now wore an obviously indisputable championship belt in the field of telephony, but
challengers continued to bob up as the years rolled
by and as the success of the Bell System was aug-
mented. The Drawbaugh debacle was followed by
a sally ventured by the "Overland Company,"
which strung wires and sold stock on the strength
of them. The Overland attack was sufficiently persistent to depress the stock of the Bell Telephone
Company and to carry its patent suit to the United
States Supreme Court, finally to be dismissed in
that tribunal.

CHAPTER XV

IT SHOULD not be supposed that during all these thrilling years of strife, development and triumph in telephony Emile Berliner's microphone patent application was having smooth sailing. It was, in fact, perpetually entangled in a serious "interference" at the United States Patent Office. Its legitimacy was constantly challenged, and its issuance correspondingly blocked by rival inventors backed by the strong corporations anxious to enter the telephone field or to develop sufficient "nuisance value" to be bought up at profit to themselves by the Bell Company. Fourteen years of these obstructive tactics ensued, despite incessant efforts upon the part of the owners of Berliner's rights, the Bell Telephone Company, to checkmate them.

In consequence of all this, it was not until November 17, 1891, that the Patent Office issued to Emile Berliner Patent No. 463,569 in response to the application filed by him on June 4, 1877. The news of the Patent Office's action was a sensation in the financial and telephone world when conspicuously published in the newspapers of November 18, 1891.

BELL TELEPHONE—THE BERLINER PATENT SENDS
THE STOCK TO 213

ran the head-line in the *Boston Globe.* "The Berliner patent," the Globe's financial article said,
"issued yesterday morning from the Patent Office
at Washington is, next to the original Bell patent,
the most important patent in the telephone field ever
issued. It covers every known form of battery
transmitter, the mechanical device behind the
mouthpiece of the ordinary 'long-distance' transmitter. The announcement that the Berliner patent
was issued sent Bell Telephone stock flying, and
from 198, yesterday's latest sale, the price shot up,
reaching 213 as top notch. . . . *We think it safe to
say, though we do not know that any of the Bell
Telephone directors, or officials will agree with the
statement, that this Berliner patent is of more commercial value than the original Bell Telephone
patent.*"

In a Washington despatch dated November 18,
1891, the day following the issuance of Berliner's
patent, the *Chicago Inter-Ocean* said:

"A curious computation was made by experts
about the Patent Office to-day as to the value of the
Berliner patent to the Bell Company. The capital
stock of that company being $15,000,000 and the
maximum rise in the stock 30 points, it follows that
the value of the Berliner microphone patent, as determined by stock quotations, is $5,000,000. On this
basis, by computation, the patent added one-third

to the value of the Bell Telephone Company's capital stock.''

It was immediately realized by all concerned that the issuance of the Berliner microphone patent meant the continuance for *seventeen more years* (namely, until November 17, 1908) of the Bell Telephone monopoly, which up to that time had been maintained solely by the Bell, Edison and Blake patents. The public was astonished to learn that a patent had now been issued to the Bell Company, covering in the broadest possible terms the identical microphone transmitter for which telephone subscribers had been paying rentals for thirteen years, under which new patent the company would be entitled to exact a continuance of the same rentals for the same instrument for seventeen years longer. This consummation, which was of priceless value to the Bell interests, caused a furore in the country. It found vociferous expression in an indignant press. The Bell Company was now accused of having deliberately and illegitimately contrived to keep Berliner's microphone patent, applied for June 4, 1877, *pending* in the Patent Office since its acquirement from the patentee in 1878.

Encouraged by the public agitation thus engendered, and fomented by a group of ambitious politicians, mostly of southern origin, the Pan-Electric Company was organized with a capital of five million dollars for the ostensible purpose of substantiating the so-called ''modification patents'' issued to one Rogers. With these as their basis, the men behind the Pan-Electric Company, on the eve of the second Cleveland administration in 1893, induced the Federal Government to bring suit for the annulment of the Bell-Berliner patents on the ground that they had been obtained by fraud.

General Joseph E. Johnston, the distinguished Confederate officer, and hero of Manassas, was president of the Pan-Electric. A former United States Senator, Augustus H. Garland, of Arkansas, who had been attorney-general of the United States in the first Cleveland Cabinet a few years previous, was the company's counsel. United States Senator Isham G. Harris, of Tennessee, was one of its directors. Johnston, Garland and Harris were public men of spotless integrity. Their identification with the new crusade against the Bell Telephone Company sufficed to give the Pan-Electric case a serious status.

"United States of America v. American Bell Telephone Company and Emile Berliner" thereupon became the title of a bill in equity filed in the Circuit Court of the United States in and for the District of Massachusetts on February 1, 1893. It prayed a decree to set aside and cancel the Berliner microphone patent issued on November 17, 1891, and now the property of the Bell Company as assignee of Berliner.

The first round in these proceedings was lost by the Bell Company—its maiden defeat in its long and

fierce cycle of litigation. On January 3, 1895, the
Circuit Court at Boston entered the decree prayed
for by the Government. But the Bells still had on
their fighting togs, and, battle-scarred as they were,
they waded afresh into the legal fray, this time dog-
gedly to defend the ingenious invention of Emile
Berliner. On their appeal to the Court of Appeals
the decree in favor of the Government was reversed
on May 18, 1895, and a decree entered, directing a
dismissal of the Government's bill. Thereupon the
Government, no less determined to win, took an appeal to the United States Supreme Court. A motion
was made by the Bells to dismiss the appeal for
want of jurisdiction. But this was denied, whereupon the case proceeded to argument upon its
merits.

The background for the litigation had been more
than three years in the making. The sort of popular
virulence in which the vendetta against Berliner's
invention was first conceived is typified by the following editorial published in the *Rochester (N. Y.)
Herald* of December 4, 1891, a fortnight after the
sensational issue of the Berliner patent at Washington:

"For a long time prior to November 17th the
stock of the Bell Telephone Company stood at or
near $180. For about a week preceding that date, it
advanced some three or four dollars. On the Friday
before, there were sales at $193; Monday it had gone
up to $198, and on the day the Berliner patent was
issued, the stock reached $210.

"These quotations show that people inside the Bell combination knew what was going on at the Patent Office, confirming opinion long held by many that the Bell Company had altogether too confidential relations with that office. The *Boston Journal* says: 'The patent virtually secures that Company for another seventeen years in the control of its present enormous business.' The *Boston Herald* says: 'It is claimed that the patent covers every known form of battery transmitter.'

"It will be seen from these statements by the papers of Boston, which is the home of the Bell Company, that the monopoly expects to retain its grip upon this country for seventeen years longer. It has sought to accomplish this result *by the dishonorable trick of keeping up a sham contest in the Patent Office over the Berliner application through the past fourteen years. That such proceedings are possible in a bureau of the national government is a fact discreditable to the officials of that bureau during the period named and an outrage on the people of the United States. The time has come for a complete revolution in that office and a change in the laws bearing upon this question.*

"But it is possible, we might say probable, that the Bell Company will reach its Waterloo in the great battle that will be fought in the courts over this very Berliner patent. Bell's original patent expires with the term of the English patent in 1892. . . . The public will follow the further development of this matter with interest. If, in the face of all the evidence against the validity of the Berliner claim to originality, the United States courts should again decide in favor of this powerful monopoly, *these courts must expect to suffer in the esteem of the enlightened public even more than they have as a result of the litigation already had on this question. But the public, in any event, should insist upon such a change in the patent system as*

will make the scandalous history of the Berliner
claim in the Patent Office hereafter impossible.''

In bringing suit for nullification of the Berliner
patent, the Attorney General of the United States
(then William H. H. Miller) virtually identified himself with the innuendoes in popular circulation and
which are characterized by the newspaper article
above quoted. James J. Storrow, of Boston, the
learned chief counsel engaged to defend Berliner's
rights, in the course of the brief he filed in the Supreme Court, thus stigmatized the action of the
Federal law authorities:

''Naturally, accusations of fraud, made over the
signature of the head of the Department of Justice,
are of themselves a grievous injury to the persons
charged. For the public assumes that such accusations will not be made until the subject has been ex-
haustively examined, and in a fairly impartial
manner; and they ought not to be made until then.
This is especially so when the attempt is made to
throw the heavy hand of the government upon the
side of what is really a contest between patentee and
infringers. *This suit, however, appears on the com-*
plainant's own papers, to be in large part, at least,
an ill-considered and unjustifiable assault.''

In such an atmosphere began the epic of Emile
Berliner's fight for vindication of his inventive
rights in the republic's court of last resort. It
had been preceded, as has been shown, by years of
furious legal strife. ''Interwoven in the story of
the golden growth of the telephone,'' wrote John

Paul Bocock in "The Romance of the Telephone" (*Munsey's Magazine,* November, 1900), "are so marvelous oaths, such charges of corruption and treachery, such tales of ruin and oppression, such accusations against men high in the public esteem, such sacrifices of truth and honor, such disappointments and defeats of the many who have sought to share the reward of the one, that the bare relation of them all, were that possible, would surpass any romance ever written."

CHAPTER XVI

THE VINDICATION OF EMILE BERLINER

EMILE BERLINER was now to become the target of a fusillade of slings and arrows, as outrageous as any of the fortunes already suffered by the telephone pioneers. The Government's bill in equity bluntly sought to rob him of the fruits of his genius by branding him a fraud. It asked the Supreme Court to adjudge that the Berliner patent of November 17, 1891, was "null and void"; that it was "wrongfully procured to be issued by means of fraud, false suggestion, concealment and imposition on the part of the Bell Telephone Company and Emile Berliner"; that there was "nothing in said patent which contained or disclosed, or in any manner set forth," by reason of which there could be secured to the defendants "any monopoly of any patentable invention or discovery whatever"; and that all persons interested under that patent "ought to have known, and did know" that the patent was void.

On the strength of this scathing indictment, the Government's bill prayed that the Berliner patent should be cancelled and that the Government "and

148

all the people of the United States be in all things restored and reinstated, as nearly as may be, to the actual condition and state existing prior to the issue" of the patent. If the Supreme Court found that the Berliner patent was not wholly void, the Government asked that it "be treated as a contract, and be reformed, limited and modified, as in equity and good conscience it ought to be." The Government's bill pointed out that Emile Berliner sold the invention to the Bell Company before October 23, 1878, and that the Bell Company was now its sole owner. But the bill made Berliner a defendant, in order that he might appear and be heard, if he desired.

The "grounds" offered by the Government in its petition for annulment of the Berliner patent were five in number, to-wit:

1. That Berliner never made the invention.

2. That he was not the first inventor of it.

3. An alleged defect in the patent itself, i.e., that the described apparatus was not operative.

4. The long pendency of the application, i.e., abandonment in the Patent Office by nonprosecution, and alleged defects in the proceedings.

5. That Berliner's invention was exhausted under the doctrine of Miller v. Eagle Manufacturing Company, 151 U. S. 186.

The Government's proofs in chief began July 10, 1893, and were finished January 3, 1894. They consisted of the deposition of Professor George F.

Barker, expert; of a large amount of documentary evidence, chiefly the Berliner file, and other files and papers from the Patent Office; and an offer of other oral proof which resulted in an agreed statement of certain facts.

The Bell-Berliner proofs in defense began October 21, 1893, and closed February 15, 1894. They consisted of the depositions of Professor Charles R. Cross, expert, with tests of Berliner telephones in presence of the complainant Government's experts; of Emile Berliner, the inventor; of John E. Hudson, president of the American Bell Telephone Company, and of a variety of other witnesses, including an imposing array of examiners from the Patent Office. The defendants also called Messrs. A. S. Solomons, Simon and Gustave Oppenheimer and Alvan S. Richards, of Washington, personal friends who had intimate knowledge of the history of Berliner's experiments and invention, and Mr. Coombs, the patent solicitor's assistant who drew the original Berliner specification.

The Government's opening before the Supreme Court consisted, on most points, of the barest *prima facie* case. Then the defendants went into the case at large, and proved an extensive volume of vitally material facts. The Government in rebuttal attacked only one of those facts—the *operativeness* of the instrument. Counsel for Berliner contended, therefore, that it had a right to assume that the testimony developed on his behalf on all other points

could not be disputed. *The Government's rebuttal
testimony that the Berliner instruments would not
talk was overthrown, on cross-examination, by talking with them from Philadelphia to New York*—an
impressive achievement in those days.

On May 10, 1897, almost exactly six months after
the conclusion of the final arguments in the case,
the decision of the United States Supreme Court
was handed down by Mr. Justice Brewer. It constituted an unqualified victory for Emile Berliner.
It completely rejected and demolished the Government's principal contention—that there had been
"extraordinary delay" in the United States Patent
Office in the issuance of the Berliner patent, due to
corrupt connivance. It left the allegation of fraud
without a leg, or even a toe, to stand on. There are
few cases of Supreme Court record, in which the
United States figures as a litigant, that contain a
more crushing denunciation of the Government's
cause.

Having pointed out that "the delay in the Patent
Office is the great fact in the case; determined the
bringing of the suit; stands in the forefront of the
bill; was the principal question argued in both
courts below, and occupies the chief space in the de-
cisions rendered," Mr. Justice Brewer disposed of
"this burden of the Government's case" in the following annihilating terms:

"The Government's contention amounts only to
this, viz., that the defendant company was not active

but passive. If millions were to be added to its profit by active effort it would have been importunate and have secured this patent long before it did. As millions came to it by reason of its being passive, it ought not to suffer for its omission to be importunate. It must keep coming before the Commissioner, like the widow before the unjust judge in the parable, until it compels the declaration, *'though I fear not God nor regard man, yet, because this widow troubleth me, I will avenge her, lest by her continual coming she weary me.'*

"But is this the rule to measure the conduct of those who apply for official action? What is the amount of the importunity which will afford protection to the grant finally obtained? How frequent must the demand be? It is easy to say that the applications of this defendant, coming only at the interval of months and years, were, taken with the replies of the Patent Offices, mere 'perfunctory exchanges of compliments,' *but this does not change the fact that action was asked and repeatedly asked; that no request was made for delay, no intimation that it was desired or would be acceptable.*"

Dealing then with the general charge of fraud preferred against Bell and Berliner, Mr. Justice Brewer's opinion was of even more destructive decisiveness. He said:

"The difficulty with this charge of wrong is that it is not proved. It assumes the existence of a knowledge which no one had; of an intention which is not shown. It treats every written communication from the solicitor in charge of the application, calling for action, as a pretense, and all the oral and urgent appeals for promptness as in fact mere invitations to delay. It not only rejects the testimony which is given, both oral and written, as false, but asks that it be held to prove just the reverse.

"Indeed, the case which the counsel present to us may be summed up in these words: 'The application for this patent was duly filed. The Patent Office after the filing had full jurisdiction over the procedure; the applicant had no control over its action. We have been unable to offer a syllable of testimony tending to show that the applicant ever in any way corrupted or attempted to corrupt any of the officials of the department. We have been unable to show that any delay or postponement was made at the instance or on the suggestion of the applicant. Every communication that it made during those years carried with it a request for action; yet because the delay has resulted in enlarged profits to the applicant, and the fact that it would so result ought to have been known to it, it must be assumed that in some way it did cause the delay, and having so caused the delay ought to suffer therefor.'

"There is seldom presented a case in which there is such an absolute and total failure of proof of wrong."

In his "syllabus" of the proceedings Mr. Justice Brewer added:

"The evidence in this case does not in the least degree tend to show any corruption by the applicant of any of the officials of the department, or any undue or improper influence exerted or attempted to be exerted by it upon them, and on the other hand does affirmatively show that it urged promptness on the part of the officials of the department, and that the delay was the result of the action of those officials."

The Supreme Court's opinion finally set forth that the Government's "question, as stated, is not open for consideration in this case. We see no error in the decision of the Court of Appeals, and its decree, dismissing the [Government's] bill is affirmed.'' The decision was all but unanimous. Of the members of the Supreme Court who took part in it, only one (Mr. Justice Harlan) dissented. It was by a vote of six to one that Emile Berliner's rights were vindicated in the tribunal of last resort.

Thus came to a triumphant end the most important and most protracted litigation which has arisen under the patent system in this country. For years it was pending in the trial courts and subsequently was brought to the United States Supreme Court. So vast was this litigation, so immense the volume of testimony, and so far-reaching the rights involved, that it is the only case in the history of the Supreme Court to which an entire volume of its reports is devoted. The culminating decision fixed for all time the meritorious place of Emile Berliner as a master-builder in the realm of telephony.*

---

*A great deal of feeling was created against the Bell Telephone Company by the issue of the Berliner microphone patent. The delay of fourteen years in the issue of the patent was attributed to some ''adroit handling'' of the Berliner application by the Bell Telephone lawyers. True, the Supreme Court in 1896 absolved the Bell Company of any intentional delaying of the issue of the patent. Yet public opinion was so aroused that in 1903 a Court of Appeals narrowed the Berliner patent to the use of metallic contacts, *but otherwise sustained the patent*. In the face of that restriction, two presidents of the American Telephone and Telegraph Company, Theodore N. Vail, in 1918, and H. B. Thayer, in 1924, emphatically upheld Berliner as the inventor of the microphone. A metal microphone transmits talk perfectly; its range of adjustment alone is smaller.

CHAPTER XVII

CHRONOLOGICALLY this narrative of the Hanover emigrant boy who, scientifically untutored, became the inventor of the microphone, was interrupted to make place for the drama of the telephone litigation. The story of Emile Berliner is now taken up where it was left off—at the beginning of his employment with the Bell Telephone Company as perfecter of the Blake transmitter.

A humble, unrecognized and merely hopeful dry-goods store clerk in Washington only a year before, Berliner now, in the middle of 1879, was an important factor in the new industry of telephony, just staggering into its illimitable own. The first twenty thousand transmitters turned out by the Williams factory in Boston were in use in various parts of the country after passing muster at Berliner's own hands. They were known as "Blake-Berliner Transmitters." In a very literal sense, it was Berliner under whose auspices the telephone business swung into its practical stride.

Only once thereafter did it ever become necessary for Berliner again to apply himself to the

Blake transmitter, which he had successfully launched. During Berliner's absence on protracted leave, the instrument department was placed under the supervision of another man who was considered an able mechanician. But Berliner had no sooner returned to Boston than he was told that serious complaints were coming in from the Telephone Company's agents regarding the quality of the Blake transmitters. Theodore N. Vail, General Manager of the Company, directed Berliner to devote himself without delay to ascertaining where the difficulty lay and removing it.

After several weeks of plodding, Berliner, with intuitive grasp, put his finger on the trouble. He found that the substitute man who had functioned in the instrument department during his absence had introduced a new lock for the transmitter. In order to attach the lock, it was necessary to bore a good-sized hole under the casting which held the diaphragm. This hole formed an "escape" for the voice vibrations that went into the mouthpiece, correspondingly weakening their effect on the diaphragm. Only a trained and intensive experimenter like Berliner could have located the cause of this serious defect so unerringly. Once determined, it was speedily remedied. The Bell Company realized that once again, and at another critical moment, the transmitter had been saved by Berliner's skill.

The Boston of the early 'eighties offered many attractions for a young man of Emile Berliner's in-

Copyright, *Pirie MacDonald*

LETTER FROM THEODORE N. VAIL.   THEODORE N. VAIL.

JAMES J. STORROW   ALEXANDER GRAHAM BELL
GUGLIELMO MARCONI   MAJ. GEN. GEO. O. SQUIER

tellectual bent. Though he lived in a typical New England city boarding-house of the era, Berliner studiously warded off the dulling influence of such an environment and availed himself of the numerous educational opportunities of "The Hub." The Boston public library, art institute and symphony orchestra already were institutions of national repute, and at those fountains of inspiration the young inventor drank freely in his spare hours.

Work, under great pressure, in connection with the perfection of the Blake transmitter, brought on a recurrence of Berliner's nervous troubles, which only a year previous had threatened so serious consequences. In the midst of his labors at the Bell laboratory one day, he suffered an attack which required his instant removal to the Massachusetts General Hospital. The Bell Company was deeply concerned over the health of its young scientific lieutenant. General Manager Vail gave instructions that every conceivable care and attention should be given Berliner. As soon as Alexander Graham Bell learned of the inventor's breakdown, he visited him in the hospital. The consideration and courtesy received at Bell's hands did much to give Berliner courage and strength to rally from his sickbed. Within ten days he was able to leave the hospital, though not strong enough to resume work. Instead, Berliner yielded to the suggestion of Mr. Williams, the head of the telephone factory, that a period of recuperation in the New Hampshire hills would work wonders. So Berliner arranged to make his home for three weeks in a fisherman's cottage in the White Mountains. There, complete rest, sleep and life in the open accomplished their unfailing cure, and it was not long before the inventor found his old-time strength returning. It was during that beautiful New England spring of 1879 that Berliner experienced the magic of Nature as a healing agent. He remembers to this day the buoyancy of his steps as he again walked the streets of Boston.

Berliner's social contacts in Boston were limited, but notable and delightful. Alexander Graham Bell and his family invited him to their home, a beautiful house in Cambridge which the Bell and Hubbard families occupied together. There Berliner now and then had opportunity to meet the class of people who give the Back Bay cultural distinction. Under the Bell roof, too, Berliner naturally found agreeable companionship with the field marshals of telephone science, of whom Bell was, of course, the acknowledged generalissimo.

Maturity had come with his arrival in the throbbing thirties, and Berliner now felt himself definitely launched upon the coveted career of a scientist. To him it was an ever amazing transition as he looked back upon his non-technical background and recalled his humdrum life as a dry-goods clerk.

Berliner could not always hold his own with some of the trained scientists who frequented the Bell-Hubbard home. He was often embarrassed by

finding himself entangled in intricate mathematical
discussions a little beyond one who had left school in
Germany at the age of fourteen, had never had a
single day's schooling in America, and was entirely
self-taught as far as the science of telephony was
concerned. Berliner's embarrassment on this account was unfailingly removed by the frank pleasure
of new acquaintances in finding themselves in the
presence of an unaffected personality.

Berliner's perfection of the Blake transmitter
had been of so paramount importance that he was
eventually appointed chief instrument inspector of
the Bell Telephone Company. In that capacity it
was his duty to tour the instrument department of
the factory twice a day. On those occasions it was
his habit to question closely his assistant, W. L.
Richards, whom Berliner had placed in charge of
testing work, on all and sundry that was transpir-
ing in connection with the manufacture of instruments. It was, of course, of the most direct and
vital interest to the Bell Company that its apparatus should function with faultless precision. The
art, in a commercial sense, was still too young and
the public far too insufficiently acquainted with the
telephone's practicability to permit the Bells to run
the risk of catering for patronage with faulty
apparatus.

One episode, destined to be of immense importance to the talking-machine industry in later years,
came under Berliner's observation during his scout-

ing trips through the telephone factory. A manufacturer of imitation hard rubber offered to produce hand receivers for the Bell Telephone Company at less than half the price of instruments composed of real hard rubber. Vail, the general manager, turned the proposition over to Berliner, who visited at Albany the works where the imitation rubber articles were being made. Berliner was so much impressed with their beauty and the skill with which a composition was used for turning them out that he advised Vail to give the manufacturer a sample order for equipment of a thousand telephones. They were handsomer than real rubber, and, after undergoing completion in the Williams factory under Berliner's supervision, telephones fitted with the imitation rubber material were shipped to a few selected Bell agents in charge of local exchanges with instructions to keep them under close observation.

But reports soon came in that the composition equipment could not withstand rough treatment and easily cracked and broke. Its use was forthwith abandoned. But the experiment, which had proved rather an expensive failure for the Telephone Company, served Berliner years afterward, when he successfully utilized the same imitation rubber composition for the pressing of millions of disk sound records for the gramophone. Other talking machines copied this process. The identical material, with slight variations, is used to this day for disk records, showing that even an abandoned scientific experiment may contain the seed from which a great new industry is destined to arise.

Apart from occasional special experiments with new kinks in telephony, which bobbed up incessantly from nondescript quarters, Berliner's activities in the instrument department of the Bell Company became more or less routine. He had worked out the Blake transmitter so thoroughly that thousands of those instruments could be produced without difficulty and so perfectly that they kept their adjustment indefinitely. This was the more remarkable because the transmitter required to be constructed with the most minute care, whereas the Bell magneto receiver had no movable parts to get out of adjustment.

It was at this stage of Berliner's career that he conceived a desire to visit the land of his birth. A member of his own family, Emile's youngest brother, Joseph, was now in America, and, being of a mechanical turn of mind, Berliner secured for him a position in the Williams telephone factory. Joseph proved to be an able apprentice. One of Berliner's personal assistants, a trained English mechanic, gave Joseph daily instruction after the plant had closed down for the day. The education of his brother Joseph was part of a plan upon which Emile Berliner had been quietly working, namely, the introduction of telephone transmitters into Europe. Incidentally, he desired to give two of his brothers a chance to "get in on the ground floor" of the telephone industry in Germany.

Vail readily consented when Emile Berliner asked the general manager of the Bell Telephone Company for a leave of absence to visit Europe. The young inventor had not seen his mother and brothers and sisters for eleven years. Berliner's father had meanwhile passed away. Even in the days of his slender income as a store clerk in Washington, Berliner had regularly sent money to his mother, in accordance with the time-honored practise of the millions of young Europeans who emigrated to these treasure shores.

Early in the summer of 1881 Berliner went back to Germany, under vastly different circumstances than those which marked his departure from Hanover in 1870, an emigrant youth possessing little but dormant talent with which to start life in a new and strange land. Berliner had by now profited handsomely from his telephone inventions, though his rewards were wholly incommensurate with the returns which inventive achievements like the transmitter would bring to-day. Yet the Bells had given him what was a fortune for those times—nearly fifty years ago. His financial prosperity was, of course, a gratifying testimonial to his merit, but he derived immensely greater satisfaction from the scientific recognition his struggles had brought him.

Berliner's widowed mother no longer occupied the house in Hanover which had sheltered him and

his brothers and sisters in their youth. Four
brothers and two sisters were still alive, some married, others making their home with their mother.
Hanover otherwise was much the same. The city
was throbbing with the new industrial energy which
came to Germany after the victorious war with
France and was the seat of prosperous factories of
various sorts. One of its budding new industries
was a rubber works in which a comrade of Berliner's school days, Herman Hecht, was prominent.
The inventor's mother rejoiced in the reunion with
her son after the lapse of ten years, and in his triumphant entry into the newly world-famed science
of telephony. Day after day, for the edification of
his mother, brothers, sisters and old friends, Berliner had to hold forth in minute description of his
life and work in "free America." In the eyes of
them all he assumed the dimensions of a hero. What
most astonished them, steeped as they were in German tradition, was that success in life was possible
without influence, and, in a scientific profession,
without university training. Berliner's achievement, accomplished wholly because of natural ability and the will to do, struck his Hanoverian kin
and former associates as little short of miraculous.

The Bell magneto telephone was already known
in Germany. To a limited extent it was in use in
various government departments, principally by
the post-office. The largest electric concern of the
time, the firm of Siemens and Halske, of Berlin, was

manufacturing an enlarged Bell magneto telephone. This was used both as a receiver and a transmitter, but no battery transmitter was employed.

The young American saw at once the opportunity for introduction in Germany of the telephone transmitter, or microphone, and the establishment of a factory for the production of apparatus on the lines pursued by the Bell-Williams factory in Boston. In Hanover itself there were as yet no telephones at all, and that situation was characteristic of practically all Germany.

Berliner proposed that his older brother, Jacob, who was conducting a small tannery, should form a partnership with the younger brother, Joseph, who was still serving his telephone apprenticeship in America. Emile's idea was that Jacob should be the financier and business manager of the enterprise, while Joseph should attend to its technical development. It was decided, upon the strength of Emile's persuasive confidence in the assured and limitless future of the telephone, to cable Joseph to return to Germany.

At the same time it was arranged to import a number of transmitters from the Williams factory. Thereupon there was launched the "Telephon-Fabrik J. Berliner." It soon developed into a very large producer of telephone apparatus which became famous all over Europe. Eventually it made rich men of the two brothers whom Emile induced to enter the virgin field. One of those whom Ber-

liner had tried and failed to interest financially in
the electrical business was his schoolmate of Wolfenbüttel, Herman Hecht. Hecht conferred with a
number of brother capitalists, but they came to the
conclusion that electrical engineering was still too
visionary a thing to merit the consideration of practical German business men. The Berliner factory
at Hanover was the first serious step toward the
introduction of modern telephone service into both
Germany and France. In Paris and other French
cities the "Transmetteur Berliner" was for years
afterward the standard instrument. So the Hanover lad paved the way for the telephone transmitter or microphone in the Old World, as he had done
in the New.

Having accomplished his ambition to start his
brothers in the telephone business, Emile devoted
the rest of his sojourn in Germany to recreation and
visits among the cronies and scenes of his early life.
He went to Wolfenbüttel to see the old school and
his headmaster, who exhibited him with beaming
satisfaction as a sample of what the educational
system of that modest, though model, institution
could produce. Emile invited his mother to visit
with him in the Harz Mountains, whence America
imports canary birds, and amid their picturesque
and invigorating hills, Sarah Berliner and her son
lived over again those times, fifteen and twenty
years previous when he was dreaming the "long,
long thoughts" of youth, though not faintly envis-

ioning what the future held in store for him in "free America."

In the autumn of 1881, Emile Berliner returned to the United States to claim in marriage Miss Cora Adler, to whom he had become engaged just before leaving for Europe. It was the Adler home on Sixth Street, Washington, to which Berliner once strung "telephone" wires from his lodgings across the way, and some of his early successes were achieved while thus combining experiment with courtship. A simple wedding was solemnized in October and the young couple at once set up house-keeping in Cambridge, Massachusetts, within walking distance of Harvard Square, while Berliner re-sumed his duties at the Bell telephone factory in Boston.

Soon afterward, with his assistant Richards in charge of the instrument department, Berliner was called upon by the Bell lawyers to assist Professor Cross, of the Massachusetts Institute of Technology, in the important experiments required for the con-duct of the great lawsuits in defense of the Bell-Berliner patents. On one occasion during the litiga-tion, when the United States Government's experts attacked Berliner's microphone *caveat* (of April 14, 1877) as a mere description of an unfinished inven-tion, Berliner resorted to an unique demonstration in rebuttal. He rigged up and adjusted a common telegraph key such as was mentioned in the *caveat* of April 14, 1877, but instead of using the contact

for sending a telegraph message Berliner made of it
a microphone loose contact, leaving everything else
intact.   Then, in the presence of lawyers and
experts, he caused the Government's counsel to
carry on a perfect conversation over a line simply
by talking to the telegraph "microphone."   The
Federal attorney took this conclusive test with good
grace.   Turning to the telephone company's lawyers, he exclaimed: "It does seem incredible!"

The impromptu aural proof thus supplied established the completeness and entire sufficiency of the
early Berliner *caveat*, describing the microphone—
a patent paper later eulogized by James J. Storrow
as "a classical document."

CHAPTER XVIII

HOLDING COMMUNION WITH IMMORTALITY

WHEN the Sesquicentennial throngs in the summer of 1926 crossed the great steel bridge that now spans the Delaware from Philadelphia to Camden, they found the Jersey sky-line dominated by a factory of magnificent dimensions. It has been called the house that Emile Berliner built—the home of the "talking machine."

Many men and many minds participated in its erection. But Berliner's part—the invention of the lateral cut disk record—was the corner-stone. Upon it there was reared and now firmly rests the whole "talking machine" industry throughout the world. As the telephone was impracticable until Emile Berliner completed it, so the art of reproducing and perpetuating sound remained imperfect until the inventor of the microphone turned his attention to the "talking machine."

The result was the invention of the gramophone.

The gramophone—*gramma*, a letter, and *phone*, a sound—according to Noah Webster (*Imperial Dictionary*, page 798) is "a device invented by E. Berliner to record, retain and reproduce sounds. It

168

differs from a phonograph in having a circular disk upon which tracings are made by a recording style, and from which sounds are reproduced by another kind of style attached to the diaphragm of any one of various types of reproducers.'' Berliner not only invented the gramophone, *but coined its, name.*

So terse and technical a description of Emile Berliner's second triumph in his chosen field of acoustics does necessarily scant justice to its real contribution to human happiness and to civilization at large. To have invented the microphone-transmitter, as one of Berliner's early eulogists observed, ''would be sufficient for the glory of a single life.'' But the task to which the restless scientist now dedicated his energies was to culminate in an achievement that is likely to be ranked by posterity not very far behind the boon of the telephone.

What Berliner was about to do—in his own graphic language—was to ''etch the human voice.'' Michael Angelo, with brush and chisel, immortalized the human form, but, despite God-given talent, left it—as all modelers in marble and oil perforce must do—''mute, inglorious.'' Emile Berliner took human sound, whether uttered in speech or song, and reproduced it, not as a parody as in the tinfoil phonograph or in the wax-cylinder graphophone, which were already in existence, but in accurate and fadeless form, to echo down the ages as long as time endures. He enabled mankind to ''hold communion with immortality.'' Masterpieces in oil have been

copied as etchings. Many original creations have
been made by etchers. But to *etch the human voice*
constituted a superb extension of the etching art
into the realm of physics, acoustics and of the human, living drama.

For the better part of the subsequent half-cen-
tury civilization the world over has been the sweeter
and the nobler for the entertainment and the education that came with the "talking machine."
Until its dawn, the music of the masters and its
rendition by interpreters of distinction were the
luxurious privilege of the cultured few; and not even
always of them, for to enjoy Beethoven, Liszt and
Chopin, and hear the great orchestras, the virtuosos
of piano, violin, cello and harp, or the song-birds of
international repute, meant the ability to purchase
such cultural opportunities at prices beyond the
purse of the average person.

The advent of the "talking machine," and quite
particularly of Emile Berliner's contribution to it—
the thing we know as the "record"—brought Apollo
into the homes of the children of men everywhere.

It turned the humblest fireside into an opera-
house. It taught the cowboy to whistle Wagner and
Tosti. It made Melba and Caruso the familiar companions of music-lovers far and wide. It made
William Jennings Bryan the speaker of the evening
in a myriad of living-rooms. It banished loneliness
and solitude from the life of the lowliest. On one
of Emile Berliner's walls there hangs a picture be-

neath which, in his own handwriting, are the words:
"In Touch with Civilization."

The story of that picture was once quaintly told
by him in a paper on *The Development of the Talking Machine* before the Franklin Institute:

"It shows a giant lumberman reposing placidly
on a rough bench in front of his crude log cabin in
the wilds of western Canada. Nothing but forest
and mountains surround him. His ax and shot-gun
lean against the cabin within easy reach. He is
smoking his pipe, and his faithful dog crouches at
his feet. His nearest neighbors are miles away. In
days gone by, the solitude of his existence would
have been but rarely relieved by diversions or pleas-
ures, and then only by occasional visits to the centers of supplies, where barrooms, gambling dens and
low dance-halls satisfied his yearning for a change
from his dreary and laborious daily existence.

"But now there stands in front of him a rough
dry-goods box, on it an old-time horn gramophone
and a stack of disk records. The concert halls, the
vaudeville and opera-houses of the world are represented in that pile. English statesmen and American presidents may talk to the lumberjack as if face
to face, and he can entertain his occasional visitors
with the same choice selections that are heard in
the drawing-rooms of mansions occupied by the
favored few, be they in the capitals or greatest cities
on another side of the globe."

On May 16, 1888, Berliner gave before the Franklin Institute of Philadelphia the first exhibition of
the gramophone, patented by him a few months
previous. The exhibition consisted of the grinding
out on his hand-driven machine of half a dozen

"phonautograms"—the name for records in those primitive days—which reproduced, respectively, in music and in spoken words, the following program:

1. Baritone solos: *Yankee Doodle; Baby Mine; Nancy Lee.*
2. Cornet Solo.
3. Baritone Solo: *Tar's Farewell.*
4. Soprano Solo: *Home Sweet Home; Annie Laurie.*
5. Tenor Solo: *A Wandering Minstrel I.*
6. Recitation: *The Declaration of Independence.*

Then Berliner, having electrified the members of the Franklin Institute with alluring evidence of the gramophone's present, invited them to accompany him on a prophetic tour into the field of its future. Here is his flight into fancy thirty-eight years ago, long before the needles of the talking machine had scratched the surface of its possibilities:

"A standard reproducing apparatus, simple in construction and easily manipulated, will, at a moderate selling price, be placed on the market.

"Those having one may then buy an assortment of Phonautograms, to be increased occasionally, comprising recitations, songs, chorus and instrumental solos or orchestral pieces of every variety.

"In each city there will be at least one office having a gramophone recorder with all the necessary outfits. There will be an acoustic cabinet, or acousticon, containing a very large funnel or other sound concentrator, the narrow end of which ends in a tube leading to the recording diaphragm. At the wide opening of the funnel will be placed a piano, and back of it a semicircular wall for reflecting the sound into the funnel. Persons desirous of having their voice taken will step before the funnel and, upon a given signal, sing or speak, or they may perform upon an instrument. While they are waiting the plate will be developed, and when it is satisfactory, it is turned over to the electrotyper or to the molder in charge, who will make as many copies as desired.

"Prominent singers, speakers or performers may derive an income from royalties on the sale of their phonautograms, and valuable plates may be printed and registered to protect against unauthorized publication.

"Collections of phonautograms may become very valuable, and whole evenings will be spent at home going through a long list of interesting performances. Who will deny the beneficial influence which civilization will experience when the voices of dear relatives and friends long departed, the utterances of the great men and women who lived centuries before, the radiant songs of Patti, Campanini, and others, the dramatic voices of Booth, Irving and Bernhardt, and the humor of Nye and Riley can be heard and reheard in every well-furnished parlor.

"Last wills can be registered with the testators' own voices, and important testimony can be sent from afar and read in court, and the voice so produced can be testified to by friends present.

"Languages can be taught by having a good elocutionist speak classical recitations, and sell copies of his voice to students. In this department alone, and that of teaching elocution generally, an immense field is to be filled by the gramophone.

"Addresses—congratulatory, political or otherwise—can be delivered by proxy so loudly that the audience will be almost as if conscious of the speaker's presence.

"A singer unable to appear at a concert may

send her voice and be represented as per program, and conventions will listen to distant sympathizers, be they thousands of miles away.

"Future generations will be able to condense within the space of twenty minutes a tone picture of a single lifetime. Five minutes of a child's prattle, five of the boy's exultations, five of the man's reflections, and five from the feeble utterances from the death-bed. Will it not be like holding communion even with immortality?"

CHAPTER XIX

BIRTH OF THE TALKING MACHINE

IT IS a curious coincidence that although it was in America that both the telephone and the talking machine were actually invented and perfected, it was from France that the fundamental ideas underlying each of them sprang.

Charles Bourseuil, a Frenchman, first evolved the theory of sending speech by telegraph in 1854. Another Frenchman, Leon Scott, invented in 1857 the first instrument for recording, though not reproducing, the vibrations of the human voice and of musical instruments. Scott's device was the "phonautograph." This is usually regarded as a precursor of the "talking machine," even though it had little in common with the instrument we know to-day by that name. Scott's phonautograph could only register sound, which was projected against a diaphragm and recorded on a moving cylinder around which paper covered with lampblack was wrapped. A lever or stylus was attached to the diaphragm, and this stylus traced the record on the smoked paper.

What makes a talking machine talk? Emile Berliner answers the question tersely and clearly. "Fundamentally it is this," he says. "Sound thrown against a diaphragm makes it vibrate. If a needle is attached to the center and made to touch a moving surface, for instance, semi-hard wax, the point of the needle will trace or cut sound vibrations into the wax. This is called *a sound record*. If now the diaphragm and needle are made to retrace the record, the vibratory tracings previously made will cause the diaphragm to re-vibrate and thereby reproduce the original sound."

The development and history of the talking machine began with Scott's phonautograph. It consisted of a good-sized horizontal cylinder mounted on a screw and turned by hand, which gave the cylinder a slowly progressive motion. The cylinder was covered with paper; this was smoked over a sooty flame to an even film of black. At right angles to the cylinder was a large-sized barrel-shaped horn which was closed by a diaphragm and to the center of the diaphragm was fixed a flexible bristle, so adjusted that the point of the bristle just touched the smoked surface. When the cylinder was turned any sound uttered into the barrel traced sound waves into the sooty surface. The phonautograph was one of the first machines utilizing a diaphragm for visual studies of a voice record. In the National Museum at Washington there is an old original Scott Phonautograph which Professor Joseph Henry used in his studies of sound vibrations.

During the summer of 1877, when America's attention was still riveted on the speaking telephone, and on all and sundry connected with that miracle, Edward H. Johnson, who was associated with Thomas A. Edison, embarked upon a lecture tour devoted to the public presentation of past and prospective achievements in technical science, especially electro-magnetics. A considerable portion of Mr. Johnson's lecture consisted of a description of a device which Edison had worked out. By means of it the inventor thought it would be possible to send a mechanically registered voice message to any of the few Bell telephone stations then in operation, and thence have it transmitted automatically over wires. This process would have been the equivalent of sending the usual written message by telegraph.

Edison's idea was to mount a diaphragm and a stylus, or needle, against a moving strip of paper, talk the message to the diaphragm, and let the stylus indent the moving strip, with the characters of speech appearing as a continuous groove containing these up-and-down indentations. The strip was to be sent to the telephone station and passed over a transmitter on the diaphragm of which was another stylus. This stylus followed the voice indentations and thereby caused voice undulations in the current, as if some one had spoken to the transmitter directly. Thus the message could be sent by a sort of automatic telephone repeater.

According to the testimony of Edward H. Johnson, contained in an address published in the *Electrical World,* New York, on February 22, 1890, the graphic term "talking machine" was not the invention of Mr. Edison, but of a clever head-line writer on a Buffalo newspaper.

"In the course of one of my lectures, or improvised talks," Mr. Johnson narrated, "it occurred to me that it would be a good idea to tell my audience about Edison's telephone repeater, at Buffalo, which I did. My audience seemed to have a much clearer appreciation of the value of the invention than we had ourselves. They gave me such a cheer as I have seldom heard. I did not comprehend the importance of the device at the time; but the next morning the Buffalo papers announced in glaring head-lines:

'A Great Discovery: A Talking Machine by Professor Edison. Mr. Edison's Wonderful Instrument Will Produce Articulate Speech With All the Perfections of the Human Voice.'

"I realized for the first time that Edison had, as a matter of fact, invented *a talking machine.* The immediate importance of it to me was that this created a sensation, and I had very large audiences in all my entertainments thereafter. Realizing that and having had sufficient experience by this time to profit by such things, I made a special point of this feature in my next entertainment, which was at Rochester, and I had a crowded house—one that did my heart good—and my pocket, too. That satisfied me that I had better go home and assist in perfecting this instrument.

"I knew, from my own experience in the matter, that it was a comparatively simple thing to do, so I canceled thirteen engagements and went back home with those newspaper clippings. I went straight down to the laboratory, which was then at Newark, and I said: 'Mr. Edison, look here. See the trouble you have got me into.' He read these things over and said: 'That is so; they are right. This is what it is—a talking machine.' I said: 'Can you make it?' He said, 'Of course. Have you got any money?' I said, 'Yes, I have a little,' and I had a little. He said: 'Go to New York and get me three feet of stub steel an inch and a half in diameter, and a piece of brass pipe four inches in diameter and six or eight inches long, and we will make it.'

"I took the next train to New York and got the material and took it back and went to work. Within twenty-four hours we had a little revolving cylinder turned with a crank and a simple diaphragm needle, wrapped a sheet of tinfoil around the cylinder, and gave it the original phonographic sentence, 'Mary Had a Little Lamb.' Then we sat back, to see what the instrument was going to do about it. It came out to our entire satisfaction. Not as clear as it does to-day, but it was 'Mary Had a Little Lamb' sure enough. *That was, the original phonograph.*"

This happened in the fall of 1877. It is, however, a matter of record that Charles Cros, a Frenchman, as early as April thirtieth of that year, actually deposited with the Academy of Sciences in Paris a sealed envelope containing a document in which Cros described a fundamental idea for reproducing speech from a record of the voice previously made on a moving surface. The contents were described as "A Process of Recording and Reproducing Audible Phenomena." It was not until December 3, 1877, that the Cros paper was divulged in an open discussion of the Academy of Sciences. Meantime Edison appeared with the phonograph.

The Edison tinfoil cylinder phonograph was presently exhibited all over the world. To be sure, the reproduction it made was little better than a parody of the voice. Every indentation made by the voice was changed by the wave and the indentation following it, because the tinfoil readily yielded to direct or adjoining pressure. The inevitable result was a general distortion of the record. But as a scientific and ingenious curiosity the original tinfoil phonograph ranked high, even though after a few years it was forgotten by the public at large.

A year or two after the invention of the telephone Alexander Graham Bell received from the French Government a gift of money, known as the Volta Prize, for the invention of the telephone.* With the money Bell built and equipped the Volta Laboratory in Washington for the purpose of carrying on scientific research, in particular in matters relating to sound and acoustics.

Among the men engaged to conduct the Volta Laboratory were Alexander Graham Bell's cousin, Chichester A. Bell, and Charles Sumner Tainter.

Bell and Tainter agreed that it might be pos-

---

*Alessandro Volta in 1800 made the first electric cell. His battery, or ''voltaic pile,'' consisted of a number of silver coins and an equal number of zinc disks of the same size. The silver and zinc disks were piled alternately on top of one another, with pieces of moist cloth between the disks. Wires were fastened to the top and bottom of the pile, and, when they were joined, Volta obtained a steadily flowing current of electricity. Thus did electrical engineering begin. [*A Popular History of American Invention.*]

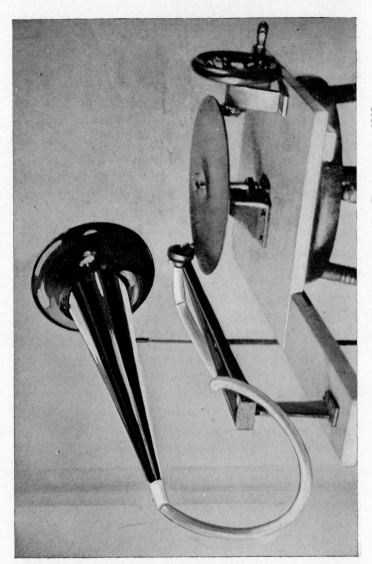

First Disk Talking Machine (Gramophone). Exhibited in 1888

GRAMOPHONE SOUND TRACINGS

GRAMOPHONE REPRODUCER, 1889

GRAMOPHONE RECORDER, 1888

sible to improve the Edison tinfoil phonograph so as to make it a serviceable "talking machine." After endless experimental work, they finally decided that distortion of the voice recorded by indenting the vibration into tinfoil might be avoided if, instead, the voice vibrations were *cut* into wax or a wax-like substance by a very small, sharp chisel attached to the center of a diaphragm. Their reasoning was thoroughly logical and scientific. Forthwith the process that was evolved from it, *viz.*, a wax record cut with a chisel, produced a vast improvement over the Edison record indented into tinfoil. Bell and Tainter received a patent for it on May 4, 1886.

In the spring of 1887 the Bell-Tainter instrument, which they had christened "graphophone," was first exhibited. It was the first really practical apparatus of the phonograph type and excited the animated admiration of crowds in Washington and other places where it was displayed. The American Graphophone Company was organized by Philadelphia capitalists to exploit the machine. The company established a factory and embarked commercially upon the production of talking machines and of wax-covered paper-cylinder records.

Berliner's Franklin Institute address on the gramophone, in June, 1888, contained the following paragraph:

"Soon after the graphophone became generally known, Mr. Edison took again to experimenting with the phonograph, and also settled upon a cylinder of wax and the graving-out process, thus confirming the correctness of the Bell-Tainter conclusions. *The new Edison phonograph and the graphophone appear to be practically the same apparatus, differing only in form and motive power.*"

It was the cylinder type of talking machine that finally developed into the dictaphone, a form of wax-cylinder graphophone now in so common use in offices for stenographic and typing purposes, and frequently impressed into the service of the detective's mysterious art.

CHAPTER XX

IN 1883 Emile Berliner and his bride, after two years of honeymoon existence within the cultured shadow of "fair Harvard" at Cambridge, resumed their residence in Washington. Berliner had come to the conclusion that the National Capital, besides being the country's political metropolis, was also its scientific hub. The Smithsonian Institution and the United States Patent Office were there. Intellectual achievement in America, in countless directions, has had its origin and inspiration on the Potomac, the atmosphere of which, of course, had for Berliner in addition the sentimental charm of the environment in which success in his chosen profession came to the inventor of the microphone. Washington, in the days of the Arthur administration, was still a horse-car town, with few indications of its impending twentieth-century importance and grandeur. But Berliner decided, all things considered, that it was the natural place in which to pitch his tent.

One of the recognized captains of the new telephone industry at thirty-two years of age, and with a competence that was more than comfortable for conditions of the time, Berliner might easily have quit the anxious and arduous field of inventive endeavor, and rested leisurely upon his telephone laurels. No thought was remoter from his desires or intentions. His telephonic studies had familiarized him with all the causes influencing the transmission and reproduction of the voice. The idea of devising something that would perfectly record human sound seemed to him like a natural sequel to the art of telephony, to the success of which Berliner had contributed so substantially. He determined forthwith to devote himself to the invention of a talking machine on original lines.

Now a full-fledged citizen of the United States and the head of a family, Berliner's first objective in Washington was the establishment of a home. Forty-three years ago the Columbia Heights section of the capital was a suburban region that suggested a passion for solitude on the part of any one who built there. But Berliner was not dissuaded from his purpose by friends who advised against "going out into the country to live." So he reared himself a spacious and substantial dwelling of brick and stone on Columbia Road, only a couple of miles north of the White House, yet, in those days, a remote district of Washington. To-day, atop "the Hill," as the neighborhood is called, Columbia Road is the center of a throbbing business and residential quarter. Ultra-fashionable Sixteenth Street—"Avenue of the Presidents"—is just around the corner, with its noble row of foreign embassies and stately church edifices, and stretching in a bee-line for half a dozen picturesque miles straightaway from the White House to the Maryland line. Berliner was a pioneer believer in the metropolitan destinies of Washington and to-day has extensive land holdings acquired in times when the possibilities of the City of Magnificent Distances were not realized by many of its citizens.

In a front up-stairs room of his beautiful home on Columbia Road, which became a local landmark and was owned by him until 1925, Emile Berliner installed a small laboratory. It was destined to be the cradle of the gramophone—the term which he himself coined and which was the description applied to his machine in the application for a patent issued November 12, 1887. As in the case of his telephone inventions, Berliner evolved the gramophone only after long and persistent experiment. His family saw little of him in those plodding days and for the most part was kept in ignorance of exactly what it was that the restless young inventor was now tinkering with in his home workshop.

The old Leon Scott phonautograph, on exhibition in the National Museum, fascinated Berliner, and he had been giving it incessant and analytical study. Its soundness of theory was no less apparent than its obvious crudities. The status of talking machines in 1887-1888, when Berliner's experiments were ripe for practical results, he himself set forth as follows:

"The tinfoil phonograph of Edison had been known for ten years and was a scientific curiosity only, though of historic value. The wax cylinder phonograph or graphophone of Chichester Bell and Sumner Tainter had been invented, and its aim, as pronounced by its promoters, was to become a dictagraph for private and business correspondence. Both machines represented a system of sound recording in which sound waves were either *vertically indented,* as in the Edison phonograph, or *vertically engraved* into a wax cylinder, as in the Bell-Tainter graphophone. In reproducing these records a feed screw was provided which turned either the cylinder past the needle or the reproducing sound-box past the cylinder."

Berliner's gramophone changed all this. Its record was made *horizontally* and parallel with the record surface. By itself it formed the screw or spiral which propelled the reproducing sound-box, so that while the needle was vibrated it was at the same time pushed forward by the record groove. As the sound-box was mounted in such a manner that it was free to follow this propelling movement, it made the reproducer adjust itself automatically to the record. The horizontal record of the gramophone was more capable of recording sound in its entirety. In the vertical record of the phonograph-graphophone there was a certain distortion which became more pronounced the deeper the sound waves indented or engraved the record substance.

Berliner's attention was riveted upon three distinct phases of the talking-machine art, and upon them he proceeded to concentrate. He set out to perfect (1) a photo-engraving process; (2) a scheme for "etching the human voice"—another of the ingenious idioms which he minted; and (3) a duplicating method whereby it would be possible to make an unlimited number of records of the same voice-registration out of some tough, wear-resisting material like celluloid or hard rubber.

"Berliner's idea of constructing a matrix, enabling records to be pressed in large quantities for sale, was entirely novel," says Alfred Clark, the American Managing Director of the Gramophone Company, Ltd., of Middlesex, England. *"It is the basis of the great gramophone industry throughout the world to-day.* Without it, the talking-machine business would have remained in a dwarf state. To Emile Berliner's conception is wholly due the fact that literally millions of records of a dance number or a great instrumental or vocal masterpiece, by orchestra, band or soloist, are now struck off from the one original."

When the graphophone came out in 1887, Berliner's sharply trained ear at once discerned that, while the process of cutting the record was better than indenting it, distortion of the voice had yet to be overcome. He finally concluded that the cause of distortion could never be removed by the method of recording *up and down* into the wax, no matter how

delicately the mechanical parts of the machine might
be constructed.

For example, if one were to push a lead pencil
through and along the surface of a cake of soap, it
would require a certain amount of force to do it. It
is possible in a laboratory to measure this force. If
the pencil were pushed across the soap at a depth of,
say, one-sixteenth of an inch and at a speed of one
inch per second, it would require, say, five ounces of
pressure by the hand to do it. But if the pencil were
pushed across at a depth of one-eighth of an inch
(twice the depth), it would not take simply twice the
amount of pressure (*i. e.*, ten ounces), but three or
four times the amount.

So Berliner saw that to make a wax record by
causing the sound vibrations to cut *up and down*
meant, according to the laws of physics, that the
vibrations, while being registered, would continuously be cut out of proportion to the force used by
the voice. A distortion of the voice would inevitably
result. A more perfect method would consist, Berliner argued, in so registering the voice that the
force required to do so would prevent distortion of
the registered vibrations. He concluded that the
vibrations must all be of the same depth. From this
theory he developed what ever since has been known
as the *lateral cut record,* in which the vibrations are
recorded *sidewise* like writing. This, as Mr. Clark
of the English gramophone company points out, is
another fundamental factor in the talking-machine
art as we know it to-day.

As the Bell-Tainter patents for the graphophone covered every form of a record cut in wax, Berliner determined to go back to the original recording idea of the Scott phonautograph of 1857 and from that to produce a record groove by the process of photo-engraving. With this conclusion in mind he constructed a small cylinder phonautograph and started making pattern records of his voice on a paper surface which was fastened around the cylinder and was covered with soot from a smoky flame. He "fixed" the voice writings by pouring a shellac solution over them.

After Berliner had become quite proficient in these experiments he cut one of the paper tubes into a strip, and took this "voice writing" to Maurice Joyce, a well-known photo-engraver in Washington, who etched the record into a piece of flat zinc. Berliner then sawed off the front part of a telephone receiver, the portion that held the diaphragm, and affixed to it a stylus (or needle) across the center so that the free end of the needle extended beyond the diaphragm. To this free end he attached a steel pin, stuck a small horn into the hole of the sound box, and moved the point of the pin through the photo-engraved lines by hand. The vibrations of the voice in the plate (in this early process, photo-engraved) moved the point of the pin, which in turn set the diaphragm vibrating and thereby *reproduced* the original talk. In that manner Berliner got snatches of articulation coming as from a human voice. It proved that his general conception was correct.

After having fully satisfied himself that the lateral cut was the only logical and perfect process for correctly recording the voice, Berliner's next step was to rig up a turn-table similar to that used nowadays on disk talking machines. His machine was hand-driven, which meant the turning of a handle during the whole time a record was played, but it contained a fly wheel that insured regularity of motion. A small framework that could be moved sidewise by a screw held the recording sound box. On the turn-table Berliner laid a heavy round glass plate made for the purpose, which could be taken off and blackened over a smoky flame. The recording sound box was carefully adjusted, so that an elastic stylus just touched the smoky surface of the glass plate. In this manner a flat disk record was finally produced. After the record had been "fixed" by shellac varnish, Berliner took it to Joyce, who quickly turned out the first flat disk-record made by the photo-engraving process. This historic "pancake" has an honorable place among scientific relics in the National Museum at Washington.

While Berliner reproduced from this first disk record, he noticed that even when he disengaged the screw mechanism the record groove itself would hold the stylus of the sound box. Immediately he realized that in voice reproducing the screw mechanism could be discarded. It has never been used since then.

Besides its reproducing superiority, the gramo-

phone mechanism was of materially greater simplicity. For reproducing a phonograph-graphophone
record, because it was done in a soft material, a fine
screw mechanism was required to propel the reproducing sound box and stylus needle across the
record lines. In the gramophone record, which was
in hard material like metal or composition, the
record disk is merely revolved; the needle of the
sound box is dropped into the groove, and this, while
playing the music, not only vibrates the diaphragm
(throwing the music into the horn), but also propels
the needle across the record disk at the same time.
It will be seen that this *automatic* propulsion is
necessarily smoother than where propulsion is
caused by an outside, unrelated force. The self-
propulsion which Berliner originated was eventually
applied to all existing talking machines as soon as
Berliner's patent expired in 1912.

Early in 1888 Berliner fitted up a couple of
rooms on G Street, not far from the quarters he
occupied when he invented the microphone eleven
years before. He needed a more central location for
his busy workshop and now continued his researches
within the shadow of the United States Patent Office.
Preceding an address which Berliner made there in
March, 1926, before four hundred patent examiners,
the Assistant Commissioner of Patents, William A.
Kinnan, who presided over the meeting, introduced
the veteran scientist with the remark that "many
inventors had laid a brick, here and there, in the

structure of civilization, but here is a man who has added a whole wall.''

Berliner now indulged in the luxury of an assistant by the name of Werner Suess, who once worked for Robert Wilhelm von Bunsen, a professor at Heidelberg University. A noted chemist and physicist, von Bunsen in 1855 invented the burner which bears his name. Since then it has been possible to burn coal gas with an intensely hot and smokeless flame. Everybody who lights an ordinary gas stove is putting to work a series of Bunsen burners. Suess was the man who constructed one of the two induction coils Berliner used when, years before, he had fashioned his triumphant telephone apparatus. He was older than Berliner—a quaint, stocky, sturdy, ruddy-faced, bespectacled German and had been a close student of Berliner's work during the intervening years. Suess, though only a mechanic, was full of intelligent interest and enthusiasm. He was also addicted to telling stories and the little Berliner laboratory was not exclusively an arena of scientific discussion.

Emile Berliner was now sure that a perfected disk talking machine had a great future, and that records for such a machine could be duplicated endlessly, provided the process was carefully worked out. That became his next objective.

CHAPTER XXI

ETCHING THE HUMAN VOICE

ON May 16, 1888, six months after the issuance of his gramophone patent, Emile Berliner gave the first public exhibition of his ingenious method of "etching the human voice." The scene of that epoch-making event, as befitted its scientific importance, was the Franklin Institute at Philadelphia, which had invited Berliner to read at one of its stated meetings a paper on his latest achievement in acoustics.

To that famed American clearing-house for the display and elucidation of the newest things in science, Berliner, accompanied by the faithful and rotund Suess, trundled through the streets of the Centennial City a strange collection of paraphernalia, including the gramophone recorder, the recording diaphragm and stylus, and the reproducing apparatus.

It was universally realized that both the telephone and the talking machine, although they had long since ceased to be novelties, were only in their swaddling clothes. Men with vision recognized and discerned their illimitable possibilities, but these were yet to emerge. The Franklin Institute's interest in what Berliner had to reveal in the talking-machine field was correspondingly eager. At the old graystone building on South Seventh Street, a still existing symbol of the Philadelphia of intellectual tradition, Berliner and Suess found the little amphitheater-like auditorium packed to its farthermost seat with some four hundred men and women on the tiptoe of expectancy.

Curiosity was particularly keen with regard to the inventor's process of recording sound waves, whereby the human voice was captured, imprisoned in enduring metal, liberated at will, and then locked up again. Spoiled, matter-of-fact moderns, addicted to the habit of taking miracles for granted, can only imagine the sensation which Berliner's gramophone concert caused at Philadelphia. It was the début of "canned music"—John Philip Sousa's celebrated description of the talking-machine art. To-day, directly across the Delaware from Philadelphia at Camden, "His Master's Voice," thanks to Emile Berliner's pioneer achievement, is reproduced in millions of exemplars for the entertainment and the education of the civilized universe. In May, 1913, on the twenty-fifth anniversary of his first exhibition of the gramophone on its premises, the Franklin Institute awarded Berliner its highest honor— the Elliott Cresson gold medal "in recognition of important contributions to telephony and to the science and art of sound reproduction." On the same occasion medals were presented to Charles Proteus Steinmetz "for achievements in the field of electrical engineering"; to Lord Rayleigh, of England, "for researches in physical science," and to Emil Fischer, of Berlin, "for contributions to the science of organic and biological chemistry."

The lesson of simplicity which the telephone was continuously preaching caused Berliner at an early date to look for a simpler plan to attain his purpose in connection with the talking machine. In the specification originally filed by him at the United States Patent Office, he said: "This record [meaning the phonautogram] may then be engraved either mechanically, chemically, or photo-chemically." Although for a long time without much hope for success, the idea of the purely chemical process of direct etching haunted him continuously, and was repeatedly suggested by others.

It was more easily suggested than carried out. Under the principles of the gramophone the etching ground was to offer practically no resistance to the stylus. To construct a ground which had no resistance mechanically, but would resist the etching fluid after the tracing was done, was the problem to be solved.

"You will readily see," Berliner told his Franklin Institute audience in May, 1888, "that if we can cover, for instance, a polished metal plate with a delicate etching ground, trace in this a phonautogram, and then immerse the plate in an etching fluid, the lines will be *eaten in,* and the result will be a groove of even depth, such as is required for reproduction. Such a process, of course, would be much more direct and quicker than the photo-engraving method.

"In nature provision seems to be made for all the wants of mankind. Confident in this belief, I kept on trying to find a trail which would lead to promising results, and I have the honor to-night, for the first time, to bring before you this latest achievement in the art of producing permanent sound records from which a reproduction can be obtained, if necessary, within fifteen or twenty minutes, and which can be accurately multiplied in any number by the electrotype process. It may be termed, in short, *the art of etching the human voice.*"

The etching ground which Berliner used was a fatty ink. One of the best inks he discovered was made by digesting pure yellow beeswax in cold gasoline or benzine. Benzine in a cold state did not dissolve all the elements of the wax, but only a small part—namely, that which combined with the yellow coloring principle. The resultant and decanted extract was a clear solution of a golden hue, which gradually became bleached by exposure to light. The proportions Berliner employed were one ounce of finely scraped wax to one pint of gasoline.

He then took a polished metal plate—generally zinc—and flowed the fluid on and off, as if he were coating with collodion. The benzine quickly evaporated and there remained a very thin layer of wax fat, iridescent under reflected light, not solid as a coating produced by immersion in a melted mass, but spongy or porous, and extremely sensitive to the lightest touch. Partly on account of the too great sensitiveness of a single film, and also as an additional protection against the action of the acids employed in the subsequent etching, Berliner applied a second coating of the solution. This double coat, he found, answered all requirements.

With many weeks of tedious experiment behind him, Berliner now took a number of zinc disks, had them highly polished, cleaned the surface with gasoline, warmed them and poured the yellow fat solution over them. In the meantime he had constructed a turn-table machine on which the prepared zinc disk could be mounted and revolved at regular speed, while a small reservoir of alcohol dripped the fluid on the fatty film. The previously used phonautographic recording sound box and stylus were mounted over the disk so that the point of the stylus cut through the fatty film. The whole mechanism was given a progressive motion, so that when the disk was rotated the stylus of the sound box inscribed a spiral line into the fatty film. If now somebody spoke into the phonautographic sound box, the line in the fatty film assumed the wavy forms of the sound vibrations; and when the record disk was immersed into the acid solution the record lines were *etched* into the zinc, forming a groove of

even depth and *varying direction* as distinguished
from the phonograph-graphophone record consisting of a groove of *straight direction,* but of *varying
depth.*

By the early spring of 1888 Berliner had made
sufficient progress to enable him to manufacture
modern disk sound records out of zinc plates. To
make records, he invited pianists, violinists, singers
and lecturers to his laboratory. One day a couple of
Spaniards arrived with an introduction from a mutual friend. They wanted to see the gramophone in
action. Berliner had just made an exceptionally
good record of a coloratura soprano, and he played
it for his temperamental callers, placing them directly in front of the horn. One of them, a black-
eyed, fiery South American, became very excited,
as the amorous tones of the invisible prima donna
emerged from a mysterious somewhere. When the
singer finished, on a beautiful high trill, the Span-
iard, all enraptured, turned to Berliner and enthusiastically exclaimed: *"Oh, I could just kees her!"*

Once Berliner's father-in-law waited outside of
the laboratory because he heard the inventor speaking as if engaged in making a record. When the
monologue was finished, Mr. Adler walked in, and,
to his surprise, found that Berliner had not spoken
at all, but was merely playing a record of his own
voice. Experiences like these convinced Berliner
that he was on the high road to practical results
with the gramophone.

The Franklin Institute exhibition proved to be the forerunner of a tremendous activity and of a development in the talking-machine industry that has not halted to this day. Berliner had thus far been able to display original first records only, although at Philadelphia he showed a duplicate made by the ordinary electrolysis process. As soon as he and Suess returned to Washington, Berliner set his whole mind to work on a feasible and practical method for making unlimited duplicates from an original disk. He soon matured a general plan which consisted of making of an original zinc record a perfect reverse or matrix by the process of electrotyping. This showed the record lines raised over the surface of the disk. The reverse matrix was to be used for impressing the record lines on some softened material like hard rubber and celluloid, exactly as seals are made by impressing an engraved letter or design into sealing wax.

Berliner encountered endless difficulties in trying to produce an accurate reverse of an original zinc record, because unless the matrix, down to its very surface, was a faithful reproduction, the reverse would not be sufficient to answer the demand for accurate sound copies. It was four years before Berliner finally succeeded in perfecting matrices with complete certainty from any zinc record.

In this important work of developing absolute sound copies in unlimited numbers, Berliner had the cooperation of Max Levy, of Philadelphia, a technician of great ability. Levy was the well-known inventor and first manufacturer of the glass-ruled screens used all over the world in making half-tone reproductions of photographs. By 1892 perfect matrices were obtained. It was found that after the copper surfaces were nickel-plated they could be impressed without deterioration into hard rubber, celluloid, or composition previously softened by heat.

It seemed to all concerned as if the gramophone with its flat disk duplicate records was now ready for commercial exploitation. The Berliner Gramophone Company of Philadelphia in fact began to manufacture small hand-driven machines and asked Berliner to make in Washington an assortment of records comprising a sufficiently varied repertoire to satisfy a small popular demand. Then a serious hitch occurred. The hard-rubber concern, which had undertaken to press as many records as might be demanded from the matrices furnished by Berliner, found that it could not produce records of even quality. There were flat places here and there, caused by gases developed by the rubber when heated, which rendered the whole output unreliable.

At this critical stage Berliner recalled the unsuccessful attempt in 1879 of the Bell Company to utilize an imitation rubber composition for a cheaper hand telephone. Berliner now approached a manufacturer of imitation hard rubber and furnished him with a gramophone matrix. Within a week the manufacturer supplied a dozen perfect disk records. Ever since then, the countless millions of disk records sold annually throughout the world have been made from a similar material. The base of the composition is shellac, which is also the base of sealing wax, and it is literally correct to say that a modern disk record is *a seal of the human voice*.

In the practise worked out by Berliner, and followed to this day, a lump of shellac composition material was softened by heat. It was placed under a matrix in a power-press. The applied pressure spread the composition and pressed the lines of the matrix into it. The matrix and the pressed composition copy were then chilled. A hard composition copy was the result.

Thus for the first time in the history of talking machines was solved the problem of making unlimited copies of one original record. Berliner had laid the foundations of a business of gigantic dimensions.[*]

---

[*]Waldemar Kaempffert, one-time editor of the *Scientific American* and co-author of *A Popular History of American Invention*, says:

"Although millions of talking-machine records are in use to-day, very few of those who derive enjoyment from them realize that the acoustic principle on which they are based was Emile Berliner's discovery. In other words, what is known in the trade as the 'lateral cut' record is his invention.

"The tremendous importance of the lateral cut is demonstrated by the fact that a large proportion of the flat-disk records which have been made embody Berliner's principle. Hence he played a far larger part than is commonly realized in bringing into millions of homes music and speech of the finest quality. Whatever the telephone and the talking machine may have been before Berliner's time, I think it can not be successfully disputed that he converted them into the instruments they are to-day."

CHAPTER XXII

GERMANY WELCOMES THE GRAMOPHONE

HAVING eight years earlier revisited the land of his birth with brow bedecked with telephone laurels, Emile Berliner determined in 1889 to return to Germany with the latest product of his inventiveness—the gramophone. He was still in the midst of his talking-machine experiments, but was convinced of the indisputable soundness of the theories that underlay them, and did not shrink from submitting his work to the scrutiny of men with whom *wissenschaftliche Gründlichkeit* (scientific thoroughness) is little short of religion. If the gramophone passed muster at their exacting hands, Berliner realized it would bear an invaluable hallmark. Germany was already acquainted with the Bell-Tainter graphophone and the Edison phonograph.

Nearly all Europe had become familiar with the name "Berliner" on telephone transmitters. Germany, on her part, ever ready to reclaim a native son who had successfully wooed the goddess of fame, especially in the scientific realm, was particularly fertile soil in which to plant the Berliner conception of the talking machine.

Berliner took with him from Washington a varied assortment of original zinc records comprising vocal and instrumental music. His baggage also included a complete recording outfit and a hand-driven reproducing machine. The expedition, consisting of the inventor and his young family, made straight for his native heath at Hanover and laid plans to remain in Germany a year.

In Hanover Berliner's two brothers were now operating a large and successful factory for the manufacture of telephone apparatus. In it facilities were placed at the inventor's disposal for continued experimental work on the gramophone, the arrival of which at once excited the interest of technical societies in all parts of the country. The society which had its headquarters at Hanover, one of the throbbing centers of the newly industrialized German Empire, promptly invited the *Hannoverkind* (child of Hanover) to address it and exhibit the gramophone.

Berliner received an enthusiastic welcome. A professor of the Hanover Institute of Technology, who was in attendance, complimented him upon his thoroughly scientific presentation. That was praise from Sir Hubert; for Germans of that day were inclined to view with skepticism bordering upon intolerance the merits of men who laid claim to scientific attainments without having been educated up to them through the tedious, grinding method of a specialized academic training. The one-time dry-goods clerk of Hanover had "arrived" by a route that German scientists were not accustomed to travel. Berliner's career, in their eyes, was wholly unorthodox.

The fame of the latest talking-machine marvel from America spread rapidly through the newspapers. It was not long before the German Imperial Patent Office, through Berliner's patent attorney in Berlin, invited him to display and elucidate the gramophone before its staff of examiners. The exhibition was so successful that the Commissioner of Patents asked him to repeat it before a group of distinguished government engineers and scientists. Among the company invited on that occasion was the celebrated pianist, Hans von Bülow, whose wife was a daughter of Herr von Bojanowski, the Commissioner of Patents. Von Bülow was fascinated by a piano record which Berliner had made at Washington with conspicuous success. Before the assembled dignitaries of science and the official world, von Bülow predicted a brilliant future for the gramophone. Its possibilities in the realm of Apollo, of course, particularly stirred the imagination of the German virtuoso.

It was during Berliner's sojourn in Berlin that the Electro-Technical Society of the Imperial capital, comprising the aristocracy of German scientific brains, invited him to attend its regular meeting on

November 26, 1889. One of the announced features of the program was an exhibition and demonstration of Edison's phonograph. The secretary of the society, having learned of Berliner's presence in the city, invited him to attend the meeting, and, if he desired, to acquaint the membership with the gramophone.

Berliner readily availed himself of this flattering opportunity. No one who has not personally brushed shoulders with the intellectual superiority which Prussian *kultur*, especially of the scientific brand, has since time immemorial arrogated to itself, can adequately grasp what it meant for the technically uneducated young Washington inventor to address so exclusive and discriminating an audience as Berliner was about to face. They were the *élite* of German science, expert in their various lines, and, with regard to anything new under the scientific sun, were what we unregenerate Americans to-day would call "hard boiled." Also, to venture still further into the Yankee vernacular, they were men who required very decidedly to be "shown" before they could be convinced.

Berliner was commensurately conscious that he confronted an ordeal. Uneffaceable in his memory remains the recollection of the awe-inspiring presence in which he eventually found himself that rainy midwinter night in Berlin thirty-seven years ago. On the rostrum, resplendent in his regimentals, sat the president of the society, Lieutenant-General

Golz of the Prussian Army. Other officers in uniform, who traditionally lent distinction to any kind of a function in Prussia, were present in numbers, for the German Army, even in those pre-Armageddon days, elevated science to a high place in the war scheme.

Addressing the Carnegie Peace Endowment's round-table on disarmament at Briarcliff Manor in May, 1926, Doctor Edwin E. Slosson, Director of Science Service and author of *Creative Chemistry,* said: "That Germany was able to hold out so long against encircling enemies was due less to Hindenburg than to Fritz Haber, who discovered how to extract nitrogen for explosives from the air and thus blow over the blockade. War has been virtually a branch of applied chemistry ever since the invention of gunpowder, or even from the first forging of the steel sword from the ore."

From his unobtrusive seat in the audience of five hundred Berliner observed the Edison cylinder phonograph on the platform, which, during the course of the evening, was explained, exhibited and made to perform. The regular program having been carried out, a soldier-member of the Electro-Technical Society arose and informed the meeting that Emile Berliner, "from America," was present and had consented to present the type of talking machine that he had invented. To the accompaniment of courteous applause and amid the liveliest interest, Berliner took the platform for some pre-

liminary observations before introducing the gramophone. He had carefully prepared his remarks in
German, because, though commanding the language
with fluency, he was less proficient with its technical
lingo than he had become with English scientific
terminology through his inventive career at Washington.

"To me has come the unexpected honor," he
said, "of being asked to explain the gramophone
before this society and give an exhibition of both
its recording and reproducing processes. Although
at the moment I am only inadequately prepared, I
hope that it will not be difficult for me, even without holding demonstrating experiments, for which
I lack the proper apparatus in Berlin, to elucidate
those few points which will contribute to an understanding of the mechanical and chemical processes
underlying the gramophone."

Then, in the course of a terse, modest, fifteen-
minute address, which made an unmistakably deep
impression on his audience, Berliner traced, step
by step, the genesis of the gramophone and of the
lateral cut disk record. "In conclusion," he said,
"I believe I am justified in saying, not only on the
basis of actual experiments, but from the standpoint
of fundamental principles of physics, that the phonograph already has reached the limits of its technical possibilities, while the gramophone, on the
other hand, has only begun to tread the new paths
of its immeasurable development. I leave it to your

judgment to determine whether this opinion is a tenable one.''

Berliner, with that final passage, deliberately threw down the gauntlet to the Edison phonograph in the supreme court of German science and in terms that lacked nothing of confident and frank avowal. When the inventor of the gramophone finished his address, a volley of applause indicated that his arguments had not failed to carry conviction to most of the assembled engineers and technicians. Then came a dramatic interlude.

Privy Government Councilor Doctor Werner von Siemens, the celebrated electrical engineer and founder of the world-famed Siemens-Halske and Siemens-Schuckert electrical concerns, asked for the floor. He said that ''it was certainly extremely interesting'' to them all to see these two American inventions, the phonograph and the gramophone, in action, cheek by jowl. He had himself, he explained, never seen or heard the gramophone before. ''It is extraordinarily important and interesting,'' von Siemens pointed out, that Berliner had evolved a system of recording that ''made it possible, if not even probable'' that the gramophone, when thoroughly worked out, would reproduce the tones of speech more clearly than the phonograph reproduced them. ''The gramophone,'' continued von Siemens, ''has in addition the great advantage of utilizing a record etched in zinc and therefore in more durable material than a wax cylinder. The gramophone will in consequence deteriorate less through use and better resist the teeth of time.''

Having paid this ungrudging tribute to the superior merits of the gramophone, Doctor von Siemens then said that he felt called upon to make what he termed ''some passing honorable mention (*eine kleine Ehrenerklärung*) of the apparatus of my friend Edison.'' Von Siemens proceeded: ''Herr Berliner told us a few minutes ago that the phonograph can not reproduce the voice in natural tones because the depth of the recorded impression is not proportional to the voice pressure. . . . We have, as a matter of fact, to-night heard the phonograph reproduce the voice completely and with wonderful clearness. I think it is appropriate to call attention to this essential purity of the Edison phonograph.''

''Herr Ingenieur'' Berliner was immediately recognized by the chairman for the purpose of a brief rejoinder to Doctor von Siemens. ''In my short address,'' he said, ''the reference to the phonograph's reproducing qualities applied only to loud reproduction. I did not say that the phonograph does not reproduce naturally, but that when it reproduces *loudly*, its tones are not natural. I merely wished to stress that point.''

Berliner's story of the gramophone later was published in full in the official organ of the Berlin Electro-Technical Society. To this day it remains a standard contribution to German scientific literature and part of the official history of the talking machine.

Some eight or ten weeks after the Electro-Technical Society affair, word was cabled to the United States that an Edison-Berliner "competition" had taken place in the German capital. The *New York World* received through "Dunlap's Cable News Service" and published on February 5, 1890, under the caption "Phonograph vs. Gramophone," the following despatch:

"Berlin, Feb. 4—Edison's phonograph and Berliner's gramophone were put in competition to-day. Berliner, who is an American citizen, was declared the victor. Siemens, the electrician, and a crowd of distinguished people attended."

The despatch made a profound impression in the United States. Next day's *New York World*, in an editorial note, said:

"The statement cabled to *The World* that in a competition in Berlin between Edison's phonograph and Berliner's gramophone the latter was declared the victor created considerable excitement in electrical circles. Neither instrument embodies any electrical principle, both having purely mechanical contrivances, but both of the inventors are well known in electrical circles, and hence the interest, which is intense, has been fired by the fact that but few people were aware that Berliner had entered into competition with Edison in the latter's favorite invention. It is a fact, however, that Berliner patented his gramophone several years ago, and it was exhibited in this city, Washington, Boston and else-

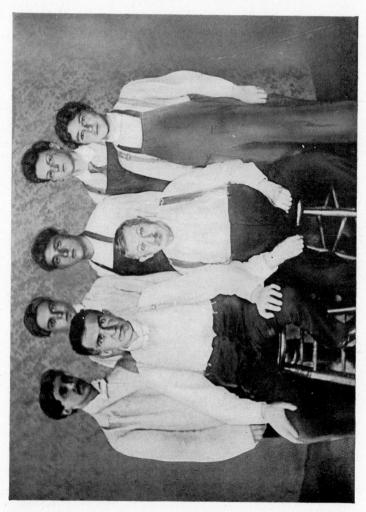

LABORATORY FORCE OF EMILE BERLINER IN 1888
SITTING IN FRONT: MR. BERLINER AND HIS ASSISTANT, WERNER SUESS

1458 Columbia Road, Washington, D. C. Home of Mr. Berliner from 1884–1924. In This House He Invented the Gramophone or Lateral Cut Disk Talking Machine, Also Known as the Victor Talking Machine

where and attracted attention, but was not considered a serious rival to the phonograph, owing to its being more complicated and cumbersome.''

The *Evening World* of February 5, 1890, under the head-lines ''Edison Has a New Rival—Berliner's Gramophone Awarded a Victory over the Phonograph,'' said:

''A despatch from Berlin conveys the intelligence that Thomas A. Edison, the inventor of the phonograph, has been beaten in competition in that city by a man named Berliner, with a talking machine called the gramophone. The sad intelligence is in a manner softened, however, by the fact that Berliner is an American citizen, and is a resident of Washington.''

A signal honor was now to be vouchsafed the young American inventor. The proceedings before the Electro-Technical Society of Berlin having been broadcast throughout the German scientific world, they attracted the attention of Herman von Helmholtz, the world-famed professor of physics at the University of Berlin, projector of the theory of the conservation of energy, and the first exponent of the meaning of color both in vision and in music and speech. Excellenz von Helmholtz was then director of the Physical Institute of the University.

Michael Pupin, author of *From Immigrant to Inventor,* whose eminent career in American science is not unlike that of Emile Berliner, was a student of von Helmholtz in experimental physics a year or two before Berliner's arrival in Berlin. "Von Helmholtz's title," writes Pupin, "conferred upon him by the old Emperor (William I), was *Excellenz,* and the whole teaching staff of the institute stood in awe when the name of *Excellenz* was mentioned. The whole scientific world of Germany, nay, the whole intellectual world of Germany, stood in awe when the name of *Excellenz* von Helmholtz was pronounced. Next to Bismarck and the old Kaiser, he was at that time the most illustrious man in the German Empire."

On the morning of January 7, 1890, six weeks after the "phonograph-gramophone" episode at the Electro-Technical Society, Berliner received at the Hotel Kaiserhof, his Berlin stopping-place, the following handwritten letter (in German):

"Charlottenburg, 6. Januar 1890.
"Marsch-strasse.
"Imperial Physical Institute.
"Dear Sir:
"I would certainly be very grateful to you if you would give me opportunity to become acquainted with the workings of the gramophone. I could not find the time yesterday for the somewhat long journey to the Belle Alliance Theater [where there had been a gramophone demonstration]. If it is agreeable to you to repeat the experiments in the Hotel Kaiserhof, I will come there the day after to-morrow at one-fifteen o'clock P. M., as I happen to be going to the city that day. May I bring those of my assistants who have concerned themselves with the phonograph?

"Should you prefer to hold the demonstration in rooms that are fitted up for experiments, rather than in hotel rooms, this can take place in a room of Division No. 2 of the Imperial Physical Institute (Charlottenburg, Berliner-strasse 151) perhaps on Thursday.

"In that case, I would only ask you to be good enough to notify the director of that division, Doctor Loewenberg, just exactly what you will be bringing along with you.

"Yours sincerely,

"H. von Helmholtz."

"Herr Emile Berliner,
"City.

Berliner informed *Excellenz* von Helmholtz that the former's living quarters at the Kaiserhof—the capacious hostelry on the Wilhelms Platz that in its day housed generations of American tourists—would adequately serve the purpose. One of Berliner's rooms was commodious and was filled, for the occasion of von Helmholtz's visit, with extra chairs.

A few minutes after one o'clock on Wednesday, January eighth, there came a knock at Berliner's door. "Herr Ingenieur Berliner?" inquired one of two men who stood at the threshold, clicking heels and standing in salute, German military fashion, as the American received from their hands cards attesting that they were assistants to *Excellenz* Professor Doctor von Helmholtz. Berliner welcomed them, and asked them to be seated. There was another rap on the door. Three more men clicked heels, saluted and presented cards. They, too, were assistants to von Helmholtz. Then ensued a succession of knocks, clicked-heels, salutes and visiting cards, all identifying their bearers as Helmholtzian lieutenants. Evidently the eminent physicist had decided to mobilize his entire scientific staff at Berliner's gramophone *soirée*.

Within a few minutes every chair was occupied and standing-room only available. Berliner counted an audience of thirty. As there was hardly space enough for demonstrating purposes, he asked the hotel to open up an adjoining parlor to accommodate the overflow. Presently von Helmholtz himself, accompanied by his chief assistant, arrived, promptly at the appointed hour of one-fifteen o'clock.

Berliner accounts their meeting one of the red-letter events of his life. It was a triumphant moment for him and one that was significantly rich in contrast—the world-celebrated, profoundly trained university man of science, the colossus of his profession, in democratic contact on the common ground of inventive genius with a self-taught, self-made man of science, who had scaled the Olympian heights with no equipment except that which intuition breeds and preseverance develops.

Von Helmholtz was on the verge of his seventieth year. He had an enormous head. His face was deeply furrowed and distended veins stood out upon a massive brow, beneath which a pair of protruding, penetrating eyes betokened the restless searcher for the scientifically unknown. His whole mien was that of a profound thinker; and his entire appearance, compellingly striking. No one could possibly mistake him for anything but a giant in the domain of learning. Von Helmholtz was partly Anglo-Saxon, his mother having been a lineal descendant of William Penn. Pupin records an aphorism of Helmholtz that has been one of the keynotes of Emile Berliner's life: "A few experiments successfully carried out usually lead to results more important than all mathematical theories."

The great physicist was cordial, gracious, natural and interested. He greeted Berliner with a kindly warmth that completely disarmed the young inventor of any semblance of stage fright in the presence of so eminent a personage.

Helmholtz and his staff of assistants were so delighted with the exhibition of the gramophone that they urged the American to visit the Imperial Physical Institute and make some gramophone records in the well-equipped laboratories there. Berliner reluctantly had to decline the invitation because at the time he was without recording apparatus.

Not long after the visit from von Helmholtz, Berliner appeared before the Technical Society of Frankfort-on-the-Main, the same organization to which Philip Reis belonged and before which the latter had many years previous exhibited his famous conception of the Frenchman Bourseuil's telephone.

German science having bestowed its august blessing upon the Berliner gramophone, German industry now turned its attention in that direction. The very first concern in the world to reveal com-

mercial interest in the gramophone was a doll factory in the Thuringian Forest, that mountainous
wood in northern Germany whence the toys of the
world once came almost exclusively and amid the
romantic heights of which stands the Wartburg—
the castle in which Martin Luther sought refuge and
threw his famous inkpot at the Devil, and the arena
of the traditional *Sängerkreig* immortalized by
Wagner in *Die Meistersinger*.

The Thuringian dollmakers said that if this mir-
acle-worker *aus Amerika* could make a zinc plate
talk, they didn't see why he couldn't make their wax
dolls talk. Berliner was not minded to branch into
the special researches and experiments which their
proposals would have entailed. But he arranged
with the firm to make for them tiny gramophones
for which records only five inches in diameter were
pressed in celluloid. Those miniature talking machines, the outgrowth of a suggestion from the
haunts of Kris Kringle, were the earliest gramophones placed on the market for public sale. The
first pressed copy of a gramophone record, produced by Berliner in the course of his pioneer experiments, was made in celluloid in 1888 and is still
on exhibition at the National Museum, Washington.

In the autumn of 1890, the gramophone having
made a triumphal *début* in Europe, Emile Berliner
returned to the United States, to devote himself intensively to the working out of details that would
perfect the machine to a point whereby its popular
appeal to the American public would be irresistible.

CHAPTER XXIII

THE WORLD SET TO MUSIC

THE sun never sets on the British Empire nor Emile Berliner's talking machine. To-day the gramophone sings and plays in forty languages. It has literally set the world to music. It is manufactured in nearly a dozen different countries. Everywhere, except in the United States, the talking machine which Berliner invented is known as the gramophone. Out of it has grown one of America's mighty industries. The gramophone does not represent the first attempt at a talking machine, as is disclosed by the account of its genesis in preceding chapters. But it turned out to be scientifically the most perfect machine and indisputably the most commercially successful product of its kind ever placed on the market.

Emile Berliner's love of music is inherent and inherited. Nurtured in childhood at Hanover by his mother, it was mainly that which inspired him to work out a machine which would essentially be a music-making machine. As a young man, Berliner studied music, and became something more than a proficient amateur at the piano and violin.

217

He still plays both of those instruments. He has always had a sound theoretical knowledge of music, and it served him effectively throughout his many years of acoustic experiment and achievement. In earlier life he sang. When Leopold Damrosch founded the New York Oratorio Society in the beginning of the 'seventies, young Berliner became one of its members and was a baritone in *The Messiah*, *Elijah* and *Samson*.

Berliner has been a composer, as well as an interpreter, of music. One of his patriotic compositions, *The Columbian Anthem*, was first heard at the national council of the Daughters of the American Revolution in Washington on Washington's Birthday, 1897. On Flag Day of the same year *The Columbian Anthem* was presented, with full chorus and orchestra, by the Castle Square Opera Company at the LaFayette Square Opera House in Washington, and sung in a number of public schools at the National Capital and at New York. On September 18, 1897, the United States Marine Band, under the famous conductor Professor Fanciulli, played Berliner's anthem as the opening number of the program at a garden party of the President and Mrs. McKinley in the White House grounds.

The *Baltimore American*, commenting on the White House concert, said:

"Considering that this country has not a national melody other than those borrowed from Europe, the *Columbian Anthem* of Emile Berliner has a good chance some day to be selected as our national melody. It is remarkable for its stately dignity and has within it that patriotic stir and catchiness bound to make it popular. It is short, like the English, Russian and Austrian hymns, and as a composition ranks easily with the best national hymns ever written.''

The Columbian Anthem was sung for several years in the Washington public schools. It was not unusual for Berliner to hear schoolboys in the streets whistling or humming his song, which was alike an expression of his musical soul and a deep reverence for the land of his adoption.

As passion for experiment is embedded in Emile Berliner's marrow, his fondness for the violin once led him into a quest for the mystery that gives an old instrument, like a Stradivarius, a more brilliant tone than a newer violin. He finally concluded that the solution would have to be found in a consideration of the uneven pressures to which the adjustment of the strings subjects the violin box. Berliner reasoned that a new violin box did not vibrate freely because of the irregular construction caused by the base bar and the sound-post, and of the fact that the four strings exerted uneven pressures on the fibers of the wood. In addition, the tension of the strings acted with a crushing pressure on the two ''feet'' of the bridge, one of them pressing lightly, the other hard and firmly. As a consequence, the fibers of the wood were hampered and could not give out the full volume of their resonance. Now, argued Berliner,

as a violin ages and is much played upon, the fibers
of the wood gradually adjust themselves to the uneven pressures of the strings so that eventually the
fibers are not compressed and give forth freer and
more even tones.

To prove this theory Berliner worked out a
method of stringing which would carry the pressure
through the center of the violin from the finger
board to the end where the string holder is usually
attached, but he abandoned the string holder itself.
The consequence was that new violins thus strung
had the same evenness and freedom of tones as long-
used violins. Berliner furnished a number of such
instruments to artists, who were surprised at the
resultant effects. Among them were Leopold Damrosch and Camilla Urso. Berliner's ideas never
attained general adoption mainly for the reason that
violinists were inclined to look upon any radical departure in the stringing of the violin as heresy, even
though they recognized the ingenuity and the effectiveness of Berliner's devices.

The monumental plant of the Victor Company at
Camden, New Jersey, is the direct outgrowth of the
Berliner Gramophone Company founded by Berliner at Philadelphia in 1892. In an *Important Letter to the Trade,* issued by the Victor Talking Machine Company on November 8, 1909, in connection
with "Victrola Infringement," these statements
occur:

"The manufacture and sale of the Gramophone was first conducted by the United States Gramophone Company, followed by the Berliner Gramophone Company and then by the Victor Talking Machine Company, which latter company acquired its rights from the former companies.

"We now control the original Berliner basic patents, and we have the Gramophone developed to its present condition. Through our efforts and improvements the Gramophone has become an important factor in the market, in spite of the general opinion among talking-machine manufacturers, at the time of its advent, that it was destined to remain nothing more than a toy."

Just as the Bell Telephone Company years before had been compelled to defend, as they triumphantly did, the validity and inviolability of the Berliner telephone patents, so the Victor Talking Machine Company for many years was called upon to take up legal arms to protect Berliner's talking-machine inventions and rights. "We have met infringement and unfair competition very successfully," said the trade circular above quoted; and, speaking of "the latest attack," it added: "We are obliged again to enter the legal arena, in which we believe to exist little doubt of our prompt and decisive victory." Subsequent events justified that confidence. The Berliner basic patents in connection with the talking machine have proved as attack-proof as the Berliner basic patents in connection with the telephone.

There is a wide-spread but wholly unfounded impression that radio, especially the broadcasting of

music, dealt the talking machine a knock-out blow.
It is entirely true that in the early months and years
of radio's vast popularity, in 1923 and 1924, the
sale of machines and records fell off seriously. But
the industry in the meantime has more than re-
covered its equilibrium and old-time prosperity. At
the annual stockholders meeting of the Victor Talking Machine Company in April, 1926, its astute
president, Eldridge R. Johnson, was able to report
that there was more than thirty million dollars'
worth of orders for apparatus and records on the
company's books and that the manufacture of one
hundred thousand records a day was required to
keep up with the demand. Radio, it would appear,
has, therefore, not put the talking machine out of
business. They have, on the contrary, become part-
ners in the eternal and correspondingly lucrative
industry of providing happiness, entertainment and
education to humankind.

In the United States alone, including the English
language, talking-machine records are now being
"published" in no fewer than forty tongues. To
catalogue them is virtually to tabulate the civilized
races of the world:

Albanian	Chinese	English
Arabian-Syrian	Croatian	Finnish
Armenian	Cuban	French
Bohemian	Danish	French-Canadian
Bulgarian	Dutch	German

Greek	Lithuanian	Serbian
Hawaiian	Mexican	Slovak
Hebrew-Yiddish	Norwegian	Slovenian
Hungarian	Polish	Spanish
Italian	Porto Rican	Swedish
Latin	Portuguese	Swiss
Japanese	Roumanian	Turkish
Korean	Russian	Ukrainian
		Welsh

In some foreign languages, such as Hebrew-Yid-
dish and Italian, more than six hundred records
have been made. There are more than thirteen hundred Chinese records, shipped principally to China,
although there is a considerable trade in Cantonese
records in the United States.

In addition to the present Victor plant at Camden, there are nine factories in the world turning
out talking-machine apparatus of the Berliner
gramophone basic pattern. The largest of them,
outside of the United States, is the works of the
Gramophone Company, Ltd., at Hayes, Middlesex,
England, which Berliner was mainly instrumental
in founding in 1899. Until 1923, the Victor Talking
Machine Company of Canada, at Montreal, was
known as the Berliner Gramophone Company, after
the name of its organizer.

The British Gramophone Company, which has an
invested capital of twelve and one-half million dollars, operates in Europe, Africa, Australia, New

Zealand and parts of Asia through subsidiary companies, branches and distributors. Branch factories
are situated at Aussig, Czechoslovakia; Nogent-sur-
Marne, France; Calcutta, India; Barcelona, Spain;
Sydney, Australia; Milan, Italy, and Nowawes, Germany.

Alfred Clark, who grew up in the gramophone
industry as a lad in the United States, became the
managing director of the English plant early in the
present century. During the World War, when all
of industrial Britain was converted into an arsenal,
the first factory to be turned completely and effectively into a shell-making works was Clark's gramophone plant at Hayes. It was also, under his
direction, the first British works to employ girls and
women on a large scale in the manufacture of muni-
tions of war. The vast park of fine machine tools
used in the construction of gramophones and records was swiftly and steadily displaced by lathes
and the other implements required for production
of shells.

It was the relentless rain of British shells that
kept the enemy at bay on the western front through
the first two and a half terrible years of the war;
and it was the ingenuity and industry of British
manufactories, like the Gramophone Company in
Middlesex, that did yeoman service in sustaining the
Allies' defense. Emile Berliner is essentially a
man of peace. In the wildest flights of his imagination he could never have dreamed that a factory

built for the production of his talking machine one day would be producing, on a twenty-four-hour shift, ammunition to be hurled across French battlefields at German troops.

It has been said in an imaginative figure of speech that music won the World War. Music may not have decided the fate of Civilization on the shell-plowed fields of France, but Song was a mighty factor in sustaining that *morale* without which victory might not have been achieved. Certain it is that the gramophone and the disk record were the unfailing companions of the *poilu*, the "Tommy" and the doughboy. Often they were all that made life still worth living in mud-soaked trench and dripping dug-out. Foch's invincibles before Verdun and the Marne reeled off *Madelon* and the *Marseillaise* on

---

*It was the Gramophone Company in Great Britain that made world-famous the dog which for more than a quarter of a century has been listening to "His Master's Voice." *Collier's Weekly*, in May, 1909, remarked that "the design has become a household word, and the quaint little fox terrier at attention before the horn is familiar to more Americans than any other of the world's greatest masterpieces." From a brother Francis Barraud, an English painter, inherited a faithful fox terrier named "Nipper." Man and dog became fast friends and one day in 1899 it occurred to the artist, an early addict to the talking machine, to depict "Nipper" on canvas in the terrier's favorite posture in front of the horn. "Nipper" was accustomed to listen as intently to the sounds that oozed from the horn as any human. Eventually the painting became the possession of the Gramophone Company. The original now hangs in a special recess over the fireplace in the oak-paneled board room of the company's head office in Middlesex. Later Barraud painted many copies of the picture, and these now occupy honored positions in various gramophone centers throughout the world.

Emile Berliner, being a painter, in addition to his many other artistic accomplishments, realized the gripping appeal and correspondingly big commercial possibilities of "His Master's Voice" for the talking-machine industry. He therefore secured trademark copyrights in Barraud's "Nipper." Eventually the gramophone companies all over the world adopted it as their distinctive symbol.

gramophone records when they were not marching into battle with those soul-stirring ballads on their lips.

Wellington declared that Waterloo was won on the playing fields of Eton. Historians may record that the British Army's victories in France and Belgium between 1914 and 1918 were won by the men who wrote *Tipperary, There's a Long, Long Trail* and *Keep the Home Fires Burning*, and by the men who made it possible for those inspiring melodies to be dinned at psychological moments into the ears of the men of England, Scotland, Ireland, Wales and the "dominions overseas," who bared their breasts to the foe at Mons, the Somme and Soissons.

How long it would have been before it was "over, over there," without George M. Cohan's haunting lyric of the American war spirit is a grave question. Troops nowadays do not tramp into battle behind a brass band. They turn on their talking machines while waiting, in soul-trying impatience and uncertainty, for the zero hour which sends them over the top. In France our men thanked God on innumerable occasions for the gramophone and for the blessings of song and reminders of home that it never failed to bring. To-day, thousands of maimed World War soldiers condemned to existence in hospitals derive their chief solace from the boons with which history will link the name of Emile Berliner—the talking machine and the microphone, soul of radio.

Berliner's lateral cut disk record, with its possibility of unlimited duplication, is the seed from which the whole modern talking-machine industry has sprouted. Since his basic patents ran out in 1912, all but two companies now manufacturing talking machines have used the fundamental principles of the gramophone. The John McCormacks, the Galli-Curcis, the Geraldine Farrars, the Louise Homers, the Schumann-Heinks, the Jeritzas and all the other songbirds, who, through the medium of the talking machine, turn our homes into opera-houses, long since refused to record for machines of non-gramophone type because their form of sound grooves distorts the voice. Emile Berliner's prediction before the Franklin Institute in 1888 that the world's great singers some day would receive rich royalties from the sale of their records long since came true. Their returns from concerts to invisible audiences probably far outstrip their actual box-office receipts. They have Emile Berliner to thank for that. In connection with accounting proceedings instituted in the New Jersey courts in June, 1926, by Gloria Caruso, six-year-old daughter of Enrico Caruso, it was stated that the great tenor's "record" royalties between 1921 and 1925 amounted to one million dollars.

The modern commercial success of the gramophone talking machine, though resting securely upon Berliner's invention, is attributable in very large degree to the supplementary work of Eldridge

R. Johnson, now President of the Victor Talking
Machine Company. An able mechanician of shrewd
technical perception, Johnson succeeded in developing a motor-driven reproducing machine which ran
with great regularity of speed, was readily adjust-
able, and, last but not least, ran silently, so as not
to disturb the sounds of the record by its own noise.
Such a motor machine had been made by a New York
clockmaker as far back as 1891, but was not quite
noiseless. Johnson also took note of the fact that
the patents of Bell and Tainter covering the method
of cutting a sound record in wax were approaching
their final term of legal existence. Deciding to take
advantage of that circumstance, he applied himself
to the elimination of the difficult etching process
and to combining the much easier wax-cutting tech-
nique of the graphophone with the gramophone
method of horizontal recording.

The new gramophone, which was evolved, instantly appealed to grand-opera stars, to the great
masters of the piano, to the wizards of the violin,
to symphony orchestras, to artists on every kind
of musical instrument, and to celebrated actors and
elocutionists. Its repertoire soon ran the whole
gamut of audible phenomena. Voice reproductions
in particular became so startlingly perfect that
hotels and restaurants found it possible to have
their orchestras accompany singers as they emerged
by proxy from the horn of the talking machine.

Presently there arose a moot question as to

whether the word "gramophone" could be patented as a trade name. In order to forestall any future difficulties Mr. Johnson coined the name "Victor Talking Machine" as a trade-mark.

The creators of the present Victor plant at Camden, by far the largest talking-machine factory in the world, have contrived, in respect of internal beauty and atmosphere, almost entirely to divest it of the character of an industrial establishment. They have breathed into it, instead, a spirit in tune with Orpheus and Apollo. Some thirteen thousand men and women are employed there in the production of everything that goes into the talking machine. In the expansive buildings devoted to the making of cabinets there is an omnipresent odor of fine woods. Artisans, apparently joyous in their jobs, hum music over their work-benches. There is visible and audible happiness rampant in the Camden staff that strikes all visitors to the plant as being in peculiar harmony with the daily task to which it is devoting itself—the mass production of instruments of melody.

Earlier in this narrative are some facts and figures that tell the story of the physical growth of the telephone. No less impressive are a few graphic details that reveal the present magnitude of the talking-machine industry.

The pressure required to press a twelve-inch record is two hundred and fifty-four thousand two hundred and fifty pounds—the equivalent of pres-

sure at the bottom of a column of cast iron twelve
inches in diameter and approximately as high as the
Woolworth Building. It would take a string of
freight cars twenty-six and three-quarter miles long
to haul the Victor yearly output. At the Camden
plant six hundred and thirty-seven thousand square
feet of blue-print paper are used in one year—
enough to make a single print over an eighth of a
mile square. Each day, for cooling presses, two million seven hundred thousand gallons of water are
pumped, enough to fill a two-foot diameter pipe
twenty-two miles long. Daily one hundred and eighty
tons of coal are burned. They would last the average
home-owner twenty-five years. If the present floor
areas of the vast talking-machine plant on the Delaware were laid out in a building one hundred feet
wide (one story high), the building would be three
and six-tenths miles long. Between May and October,
1923, sufficient lumber was cut up at Camden to
build six hundred two-story houses, each twenty-
eight feet square, and enough packing material was
used to make a two-car garage for each of them.
The monthly production of records piled flat would
make a column four miles high—twice as high as the
F5 sea-plane can fly and fifty per cent. higher than
Mount Whitney, the loftiest peak in the United
States. Edge to edge, the same records would reach
five hundred and twenty miles, or the distance from
Camden to Cincinnati. It would take nineteen years'
continuous gramophone playing to play them!

Two institutions of world-wide fame—the Library of Congress at Washington and the Grand Opera in Paris—have given substance to an early prophecy of Emile Berliner. He said that one of the missions of the gramophone record was to perpetuate, for eternity, the voices of celebrities, or voices near and dear to particular persons. In 1925 the Congressional Library decided to install a comprehensive collection of talking-machine records. As an addition to the music division of the Library, the collection is intended to give students of music an opportunity to hear the works of the great composers, as performed by master artists, instead of merely tracing them mentally from books and notes. The collection contains a large number of records made by artists now passed from the scene and is the first seriously conceived public aggregation of its kind in America.

Herbert Putnam, the Librarian of Congress, said: "The records add greatly to the resources of our music division and to the Library's auditorium for chamber concerts, and aid in giving pleasure and instruction to a highly significant public." Carl Engel, Chief of the Music Division, added: "I have been moved especially by the thought of the coming generations. To them this extension of the resources of the music division—adding to the printed record of a composition the record of its sound in performance—will be invaluable. With my pleasure and satisfaction there mingles only the regret that this wonderful invention was not made three hundred years ago."

Some time before the Library of Congress arranged to install its record collection, the Paris Opera placed in hermetically sealed vaults an assortment of records which are not to be touched for fifty or a hundred years, and then only for comparison with records made by artists still to come. Down in the catacomb-like fire-proof storerooms built by the big talking-machine companies here and in Europe, and securely barred to all but a few trusted employees, are stored away hundreds upon hundreds of copper and steel matrices, the indestructible and precious legacies which the masters of song and performance have bequeathed to future generations. Their immortality is secure.

In a paper on the Bell-Tainter graphophone, read by Henry Edmunds before the British Association for the Advancement of Science at Bath on September 7, 1888, there is a story of a young Chinese diplomat at Washington. On seeing the Bell-Tainter graphophone for the first time, he recalled a famous legend in China about a fair woman whose voice was so beautiful that her children longed to preserve it for future generations to hear. So they persuaded her to speak into a bamboo cane which was carefully sealed. The cane was sacredly cherished for several generations and then, one day, was opened. Each word came out in order and with all the original sweetness. But the voice was never heard again. It had vanished for all time.

What filial piety once in far Cathay quaintly essayed to achieve by magic has become a practical possibility in our day because of what Emile Berliner wrought. He made it possible for posterity to hold communion with the immortals.* Enrico Caruso no longer bestrides the boards of the Metropolitan Opera, but his majestic song is with us yet. Mankind has realized at last Tennyson's wish for "the voice that is still."

---

*A certain Colonel Joyce, speaking into the graphophone at Washington in July, 1888, recited the following verse of his own composition in tribute to Berliner's invention:

"I treasure the voices of poets and sages,
    I keep them alive through the round rolling years;
I speak to the world for ages and ages,
    Recording the language of smiles and of tears.

"When friends have departed, and sweet life has ended,
    Their voices shall sound through my swift rolling heart;
While all of their love-notes are treasured and blended,
    As faithful and true as the nature of art.

"The pulpit, the bar, the wants of the household,
    Shall photograph thought in the sigh of my soul;
The man and the maid shall advance more than tenfold,
    Who talk with my tongue as the years grandly roll.

"The Godhead alone shall be found in my preaching,
    And marvelous secrets I yet shall disclose.
The schools of the world shall list to my teaching,
    As pure and as bright as the blush of the rose.

"I war with the world where ignorance slumbers,
    And go hand in hand with the light of the sun.
I count every thought with quick magical numbers;
    And my work on the earth shall never be done."

CHAPTER XXIV

IN THE prefatory words by Herbert Hoover, statesman and humanitarian, with which this story of inventive genius begins, it is set forth that Emile Berliner "has crowned his material success by the capstone of a wise and notable philanthropy."

In the realm of human beneficence, Berliner, serenely across the threshold of his seventy-fifth year, is still active. As he is a fundamentalist in all things, it is to the cause of child health, which is the foundation of citizenship and national welfare, that the inventor of the microphone and the gramophone has devoted himself. He has done so not as a theorist, but as a practical idealist. As the years have failed to wither the infinite variety of his scientific activities, neither have they staled his zeal in humanitarian works, for it is more than a quarter of a century since he first enlisted in the war against infant mortality.

During the interval he has become one of its recognized field-marshals. The death rate among babies in the District of Columbia, when Berliner took up arms against it, was so appalling that, in the words of a distinguished Washington professor of hygiene, Doctor George M. Kober, hot weather saw them "die like flies." In the late 'nineties, nearly three hundred children out of every thousand born in Washington perished before the completion of their first year, principally from gastro-intestinal troubles, or an average of approximately thirty per cent. During the fiscal year ended June 30, 1925, out of nine thousand, two hundred and seventy-seven babies born in the District of Columbia, only one hundred and thirteen died from intestinal complaints, or an average of less than one and one-fourth per cent. Authorities like Doctor Kober, now the honored dean of Georgetown University medical faculty, give Emile Berliner's "clear insight" in the field of popular health education unqualified credit for the progress which Washington's vital statistics denote.

It was an attack of gastro-intestinal illness which overtook one of his own offspring, a daughter Alice, in 1900, that impelled Berliner to clear for action against prevailing methods of combatting child disease. More than half a dozen skilled physicians did their utmost to save the baby girl. But the days and weeks passed without bringing improvement. When Alice was six months old, she weighed a pound less than at birth. Only her native vitality, supplemented by starvation rations, kept her alive through a particularly hot Washington summer. At eight months, Alice was still a puny infant of eight and one-half pounds. But meantime Berliner, his scientific fighting instinct aroused, had given intensive study to a branch that was utterly virgin soil to him—child nutrition. With Mrs. Berliner's hearty approval, he took personal charge of Alice's case and personally prescribed and prepared every ounce and swallow of the tot's food.

Slowly, but steadily, then swiftly, the baby gained in weight and vigor. By the time of her first birthday anniversary, Alice was plump, rosy and of normal weight, tipping the scales at twenty-two and one-half pounds. Breaking new paths, as was his wont in the field of electro-magnetics and acoustics, Berliner had won his first skirmish in a campaign for child health that was to eventuate in a life-time crusade. To-day the Alice Berliner of those anxious years is a beautiful and healthy young woman, happily married to the young economist, Isadore Lubin, of the Institute of Economics at Washington, whose keen analysis of the British coal crisis of 1926 attracted wide-spread attention throughout the United States.

Forthwith Berliner determined to dedicate himself to the promotion of public health and the eradication of preventable disease. The ravages of infant mortality were, in 1900, not quite so terrifying as when Doctor Dickson, of England, in 1851, frantically asked: "How shall we prevent the early extinction of half the new-born children of men?" Yet, twenty-seven years later, in 1878, out of every thousand babies born in Washington, three hundred and twenty-two died before they were a year old. Mothers dreaded "the second summer" of their babies' lives as they feared the plague. In 1895 the infant death-rate in the national capital was still two hundred and ninety-seven and two-tenths per thousand. Fully forty per cent. of the mortality was due to gastro-intestinal complaints, and two and one-half per cent. to primary tuberculosis of the intestinal lymphatics.

These tell-tale figures caused Emile Berliner, on the basis of his own researches, strongly to suspect that the morbific agent in intestinal and tubercular cases was introduced into the human body with its food. In addition to the lamentable losses of child life directly attributable to impure or contaminated milk, there were recorded by Doctor Kober in 1895, throughout the world, one hundred and thirty-five epidemics of typhoid; seventy-four of scarlet fever; twenty-eight of diphtheria and several outbreaks of septic sore throat, all traceable to infected milk. The majority of epidemics occurred in countries where almost exclusively raw milk is consumed.

Berliner's course was now charted. It lay straight across the sea of dangers that lurk in raw milk. He was among the first to realize the vast importance of the fact that milk can be rendered safe by heating and by killing any disease germs secreted in it. The process, known to the world as pasteurization, was, when Berliner and other scien-

tists first advocated it, opposed by the American
Pediatric Society on the ground that children could
not thrive on heated milk, but on the contrary contracted scurvy and rickets from such nutrition. For
many years the general medical profession upheld
that theory.

How to combat the always influential voice of the
medical world became a problem, but Berliner, the
irrepressible pioneer, found the way. Convinced in
his own mind of the correctness of the principles
enunciated by a few sanitarians, he decided upon a
"Wake Up, Mothers!" campaign of wholly original
conception. In the spring of 1901, Berliner, in collaboration with a few sympathizing friends, formed
in Washington under the expressive title of "The
Society for the Prevention of Sickness" an organization to be devoted, in the first instance, merely
to the spreading of knowledge.

For that purpose Berliner engaged, at his own
expense, advertising space in the Sunday newspapers of Washington and filled it, week after week,
with what he called health bulletins. The first one
was published in the *Washington Post* of June 15,
1901, and read as follows:

MILK is notoriously one of the best soils
for the germination and multiplication of disease germs.
MANY EPIDEMICS of Typhoid, Malaria
and Scarlet Fever have been traced to infected
milk, not to speak of Tuberculosis from the
same source.

INSPECTION is rarely thorough and does not prevent contamination of the milk supply.

SCALDING (or sterilizing) will destroy most of the virulent germs, if not all.

SOME PEOPLE say that you should not scald milk for fear of making it less easy to digest. This is a very small matter compared with infection. The advice is, besides, unfounded, and should be disregarded.

ROBUST PEOPLE may with impunity disregard rules of precaution, which are necessary with weaker constitutions and children.

THEREFORE SCALD YOUR MILK.

SOCIETY FOR THE PREVENTION OF SICKNESS

The term "pasteurization" did not appear in this bulletin. Instead, "scalding" was recommended, and in the use of that word Berliner had the approval of the late Professor Jacques Loeb, afterward head of the division of general physiology at the Rockefeller Institute for Medical Research. Berliner's bulletins were intended to instruct the common people, the housewives and the cooks, who could not be expected to understand scientific expressions. The word "scalding" was utilized as meaning the use of heat without actual boiling. Boiling might make milk less digestible for infants with weak stomachs, according to the false notion then existing.

It would be interesting for modern milk sanitarians to look through Berliner's pioneer collection of milk bulletins. They were changed every week. Many authorities were cited. The whole field of

milk dangers was spread before the public. Every
bulletin ended with the slogan: "Scald the milk, and
keep it cool and covered afterward," and accentuated the fact that inspection alone was insufficient.

This method of instructing the public was so unusual that soon after Berliner began launching the
bulletins, the Marine Hospital Service of the United
States Government asked the Health Officer of the
District of Columbia whom the Society for Prevention of Sickness "represented." An adequate answer was promptly sent by Berliner.

The bulletins evidently impressed the health
authorities of the District of Columbia as early as
1903, because a newspaper clipping of July fourteenth of that year mentions that the Milk Dealers'
and Producers' Associations of Maryland, Virginia
and the District of Columbia were up in arms
against Doctor Woodward, the health officer, irri-
tated at what they termed "his unjust persecution
of their members." Two days afterward an editorial in the *Washington Times,* headed "The Milk
Problem," dealt with the question, insisting that
milk dealers must supply pure milk in order to reduce infant mortality.

Berliner continued the milk bulletins in spite of
the stubborn opposition of many physicians to the
use of heat as an immunizer of milk—an opposition
which to some extent persists to the present day.

In addition to stigmatizing impure milk, the
bulletins of the Society for the Prevention of Sick-

ness pointed out the dangers in ice-cream, butter and dairy products made from non-pasteurized cream and milk. This voluntary, popularized propaganda, systematically and efficiently conducted under Berliner's personal direction, supplied the people of the National Capital with a liberal education in the science of health. Its ramifications probably were nation-wide. What Washington thinks and does to-day, the country frequently thinks and does to-morrow, because its representatives in Congress and the great government departments are habitually relaying to the outer United States that which, from time to time, is noteworthy in the District of Columbia.

Certainly no phase of life at Washington was literally more vital in its beneficent results than Berliner's health crusade. When he embarked upon it, infant mortality at Washington was still two hundred and seventy-four and five-tenths out of every thousand children born. Not a quart of milk sold in the District of Columbia was pasteurized. In 1914, according to Doctor Woodward, the District health officer, half of the bottled milk sold in Washington was pasteurized. In 1924, according to Doctor Fowler, then health officer, ninety-seven per cent. of the milk marketed was pasteurized. There was no law compelling what Berliner used to call "the scalding of milk," but the public having been educated to demand it, pasteurization automatically came about.

In 1924 infant mortality had fallen to seventy-five and seven-tenths per thousand. Typhoid fever was reduced from seventy-two fatalities per one hundred thousand of population in 1900 to between four and five per one hundred thousand in 1924. Pulmonary consumption in the same period fell from four hundred and ninety-two deaths among the colored population to two hundred and thirty-eight, and, among the whites, from one hundred and eighty-three to sixty-two. In 1925 white mortality was as low as fifty.

"This is indeed a field of glory," exclaimed one of the reviewers of Emile Berliner's health work at the meeting of the Association for the Prevention of Tuberculosis, held in honor of his seventy-fifth birthday anniversary in 1926. "But for him, scientific facts might have remained unnoticed for a long time."*

A decided step forward in the movement for safe milk was taken in the year 1907, when the Committee on Tuberculosis of the Associated Charities, of which Brigadier-General George M. Sternberg, former Surgeon-General of the United States Army, was chairman, created a Milk Committee and made Emile Berliner its chairman. The other members of the committee were Doctor E. C. Schroeder and Doctor William H. Dexter of the Bureau of Animal Industry; Doctor D. E. Buckingham, the veterinarian, and Wallace Hatch, secretary of the Associated Charities.

---

*From parchment testimonial presented to Emile Berliner on May 20, 1926.

PROF. HERMANN LUDWIG FER-
DINAND VON HELMHOLTZ. DIED
AT BERLIN, GERMANY, SEPT. 8,
1894

DR. ERNEST C. SCHROEDER,
BIOLOGIST, DIRECTOR U. S.
ANIMAL EXPERIMENT STATION,
BETHESDA, MD., WHOSE
FRIENDSHIP AND COOPERATION
MR. BERLINER ENJOYED FOR
MANY YEARS

HEINRICH HERTZ OF GERMANY,
WHO WAS THE FIRST TO DEM-
ONSTRATE THAT WHEN AN
ELECTRIC SPARK JUMPS
THROUGH THE AIR IT CAUSES
ELECTRIC WAVES, ETC. ELEC-
TRIC WAVES TRAVEL AT THE
RATE OF 183,000 MILES PER
SECOND. THIS DISCOVERY
MADE RADIO MESSAGES POS-
SIBLE

HON. HERBERT C. HOOVER

Charlottenburg 6 Januar 1890
Marschallnfr. 17/18 Neubau

Geehrter Herr

Ich würde Ihnen allerdings 6 Uhr
Nachmittags sein, wenn Sie mir gefälliger-
weise gelegen wollen, Sie Mittwoch 8es
Januar verschieben wollen, Sie Mittwoch 8es
denn es auf Jahren nicht frei machen
für die eben langer Weise zu besuchen,
Allgemeiner Vorlesung. Nächst zu Ihnen zu
Nachmittag im Anschluß 3er gegen 1/2
meinerseits Mittwoch 2. 6. 2 N. 14
Sehr verpflichten, da ich um sein Tage
nach der Stadt zu kommen. Darf ist Ihnen
meinen Vorlesung verständigen verständigen,
Sie Prof. und Dr. Gregorieff ...
... Herren Sie ... Sie ...
... in einer 3er ...
... Heuer ...

... Ihnen ... Sie I Wolfgang
... Königlichen Waisenhaus (Verstorbenen)
... Herren Nr. 121) gefällten, ... wir
Sonnentag. Ich bitte Sie ihr Herren
wolle ... wegen In Doctor Heffe,
Abgefertigung haben Dr. Loewecker zu
verständigen. Herr Dr. Freihofen.

Ich ergebener
H. v. Helmholtz

Herrn Ernst Gärtner
Jun.

At the first conferences of the milk committee at Berliner's home, milk problems were discussed at length. Doctor Schroeder made known to the committee his recent discovery that the feces of tuberculous cows are often heavily charged with virulent tubercle bacilli, and pointed out that the examination of numerous samples of market milk disclosed that very little milk entirely free from contamination with cow feces reaches the consumer. Hence, according to Doctor Schroeder, the presence of a single tuberculous cow in a dairy herd had to be regarded as a danger through which any portion or all of the milk from the herd might become infected with tubercle bacilli.

Berliner was so impressed with the importance of the Schroeder discovery that he proposed that his committee should request the Associated Charities to call a general conference on milk problems, of sufficient scope to include representatives of the District of Columbia Health Office and the several bureaus of the Federal Government which have public-health functions. The suggestion was accepted by the committee and communicated to General Sternberg, who endorsed it.

On March 30, 1907, the call of the Commissioners of the District of Columbia for a milk conference was issued. The men invited to participate comprised most of the prominent authorities on sanitation that could be assembled from among Washington scientists and from the bureaus of the National

Government. Besides these, members of the different milk associations were invited. The Bar Association, the Veterinary Association, the Washington Academy of Sciences and the Chemical Society of Washington also were represented.

The result of the conference was the adoption of milk standards formulated by Doctor A. D. Melvin, of the Department of Agriculture, whereupon the cause of pasteurization received the strong endorsement of the Federal Government. This development compelled the American Pediatric Society to assume the defensive. As an immediate consequence, the health department of the City of New York called a milk conference in 1909, and then and there adopted milk standards similar to those previously endorsed in Washington.* To this New York conference its organizers specially invited Doctor E. C. Schroeder, Doctor G. L. Magruder and Emile Berliner, and they made their influence felt in the proceedings which culminated in unqualified approval of pasteurization.

Ultimately the proceedings and reports of the Washington conference were published by the Department of Agriculture as Circular 114. Copies of it can be found in the files of health bureaus and associations the world over. When Professor von Pirquet, the renowned child-hygienist of the Univer-

---

*Nathan Straus, who in 1892 originated, and has since maintained, a system of distribution of pasteurized milk to the poor of New York City, for years combatted the opposition of the Pediatric Society and of medical men who refused to recognize the manifest results that flowed from sterilized milk.

sity of Vienna, visited Washington, Berliner was
told that his gospel of safe milk for healthy infants
had spread to Europe and was universally acclaimed. The work of the Washington milk conference became eventually the foundation of
municipal and state dairy laws in many parts of the
country, and references to its importance can be
found in transatlantic publications, notably in England, where it received high praise.

Stimulated by the constructive achievements of
the Washington milk conference, the Society for
Prevention of Sickness prosecuted its campaign
with increased vigor. The Society, at Berliner's instigation, initiated various other reforms connected
with the milk supply. He attacked Washington
hospitals because they furnished indiscriminate raw
milk to their patients. He criticized in particular
certain children's hospitals because several of their
leading doctors continued to oppose pasteurization.

As early in his warfare on impure milk as 1907
Berliner had pointed out, in a prepared paper, what
he called "Some Neglected Essentials in the Fight
Against Consumption." In the closing paragraphs,
he said:

"Let me suggest to those humanitarians who
labor in the cause of the prevention of consumption
that no agitation is as efficient as that begun in the
Public Schools. If modern text-books could be introduced, dealing not only with the causes and prevention of consumption, but with prophylaxis in
general, it would plant the seed of knowledge where
it would bear the richest fruit.

"But such text-books would only half fulfill their mission, or indeed entirely fail in it, if undue prominence were bestowed on the hunting and destroying of the tubercle bacilli and too little stress placed upon the more important essentials for the fortifying of the human body, thereby maintaining and increasing its natural power of resistance to all diseases, including consumption.''

That was the first time that health education through the schools was ever publicly emphasized. Within a few years the Tuberculosis Association at Washington, of which Berliner was for seven years the president, inaugurated its literary campaign on the lines proposed by him and under his leadership. Three years later, in 1910, the Berliner committee began the distribution of twenty-five thousand copies of the *Twelve Rules for Health* adopted by the Association. They were printed in words of one syllable on card-board in two colors for display in the Washington public schools from the fourth grade up. Teachers would explain, and comment upon, the rules; children would take copies home, and the advice to parents, printed on the envelope, to tack up or frame the rules in the house was generally followed. The Tuberculosis Association also authorized the publication of a book entitled *Washington Health Rules*. Copies were distributed among school-teachers and, to this day, are presented to all graduates of District of Columbia normal schools.

In 1919, in order to teach the young idea as early

in life as possible to shoot straight in the direction
of health, Berliner conceived the quaint notion of
turning his *Rules for Health* into simple nursery
rhymes and illustrating them in colors for the use
of third-grade pupils. Children were encouraged by
their teachers to memorize the rhymes. Here is one
of his lyrics, entitled *The Gentle Cow:*

> "When milk is raw just from the farm
> It's full of germs which may do harm;
> But safe it is and highly prized
> When it is boiled or pasteurized
> Ice-cream, cheese and butter-fat
> Come from milk—you all know that.
> Made from raw milk, we can see
> They might harm both you and me."

As an incentive to schools and school children to
take part in the crusade for public health, Berliner
in 1920 endowed a Silver Trophy Cup, to be awarded
annually by the National Tuberculosis Association
to the city showing the largest proportionate enroll-
ment of pupils engaged in the health crusade. Berliner is a director of the National Association. In
1921 his cup was won by the public schools of Wash-
inton, D. C., and presented by President Harding.
Last year Berliner endowed a similar trophy to be
awarded in the Dominion of Canada.

In 1921 Berliner resorted to a new and far-
reaching departure in his child health work. With
the professional cooperation of Doctor Alfred J.
Steinberg, of Washington, a graduate of Harvard

Medical School and a children's specialist, Berliner wrote and published *The Bottle-Fed Baby*.* Its purpose was to inform the young mother in practical, concise terms exactly how a bottle-fed baby should be reared.

Berliner's plan was to place a free copy in the hands of every new mother in the District of Columbia, rich or poor, for within its pages were packed more useful facts and figures than ever before were issued in manuals of maternity information five or six times the size. The District health authorities readily acceded to Berliner's wish to be placed regularly and promptly in possession of names and addresses of newly-reported mothers. To this writing, midsummer, 1926, and within a period of five years, more than fifty thousand copies of *The Bottle-Fed Baby* have been distributed. Berliner still superintends personally its circulation to new mothers as fast as their names are supplied him.

This Silver Jubilee of humanitarian work and Diamond Jubilee of Emile Berliner's life find Berliner waging the never-ending war for public hy-

---

*Professor Ralph V. Magoffin, president of the Archeological Institute of America and head of the department of charities of New York University, brought back from Egypt in June, 1926, a black stone nursing bottle which did service in the land of the Pharaohs in 1200 B. C. As proof of the utensil's use for the rearing of Egyptian infants three thousand one hundred and twenty-six years ago, Professor Magoffin pointed out that the bottle is heavily constructed at the bottom to prevent tipping and has square sides to avoid rolling. The top is very much like that of nursing bottles of the present age. The American archeologist considers the Egyptian nursing bottle scientifically superior to its modern type. Emile Berliner's comment on Professor Magoffin's discovery was "There's nothing new under the sun."

giene from a three-story building which he erected
and dedicated to its exclusive purposes in 1924.
It is what military men might call a General Headquarters for Child Health. A modest sign informs
the passer-by in Columbia Road—less than a stone's
throw from the site of the rambling old home where
Berliner made his earliest gramophone experiments—that within is the "Bureau of Health Education." One of its features is a class-room where
young mothers with their children come regularly
for education, by chart, picture and blackboard. In
1909 Berliner erected an infirmary building at the
Starmont Tuberculosis Sanitarium near Washington in memory of his own father.

Restless in the achievement of constructive
works for public health, Emile Berliner in 1925, with
the assistance of Mrs. E. R. Grant, a member of his
Committee on Publications, secured the passage by
Congress of a modern milk law for the District of
Columbia, which was drafted by Doctor W. C.
Fowler, health officer of the Federal area. Mrs.
Grant succeeded in enlisting the interest of Mrs.
Calvin Coolidge, an ideal mother, who herself had
only a little while before suffered the loss of her
second-born. Since the passage of the law, the milk
supply in the District of Columbia, much of which
had been of low sanitary rating, has been of uni-
formly high standard.

Had Emile Berliner never touched the telephone
or the talking machine, his health work should make

secure his claim to the gratitude of his era and of
eras to come. The tears it has saved, the mother
hearts it has spared from anguish, can never be
recorded in the vital statistics. But that he has
made child life sweeter, surer and safer is established beyond all peradventure.*

---

*Berliner's published contributions to the literature of the con-
servation of child life include:

*Some Neglected Essentials in the Fight against Consumption;
Recent Developments in Infant Feeding; History of the Society for
the Prevention of Sickness; The Tuberculin Test as a Factor in the
Milk Traffic; The Outbreak of Typhoid Fever in Cassel in 1909;
Opening Address before a Congressional Sub-Committee on Milk
Legislation for the District of Columbia; Hospital Milk; High Ty-
phoid Mortality in Washington Hospitals and Their Milk Supply;
The Literary Health Propaganda of the Washington Tuberculosis
Association; What Constitutes Municipal Responsibility; How a
Love Kiss May be a Death Kiss; Twelve Health Rhymes* (used reg-
ularly in Washington schools); *Are Annual Winter Epidemics Caused
by Infected Butter?*

CHAPTER XXV

BERLINER AND RADIO

WHILE this biography was in the making, a letter arrived at the Post-Office in Washington, post-marked Battle Creek, Michigan, and addressed as follows:

To the Inventor of the Microphone,
Washington, D. C.

In due course, it was delivered at No. 2400 Sixteenth Street, N. W., the residence of Emile Berliner. The omniscient postal authorities of the capital city knew more about the origin of radio than the average American, to whom, no doubt, it will come with surprise to learn that, but for Emile Berliner's trail-blazing, the miracle of broadcasting—any more than the telephone—would hardly be what it is to-day.

In the perfection of that eighth wonder of the world Berliner played a fundamental rôle. Without the Berliner microphone, "the crowning achievement of the spirit of invention," as radio was recently eulogized, might still be a voice screeching

251

through the static wilderness instead of having become the oracle of the universe.

The "mike," as the broadcasting fraternity has affectionately dubbed the microphone, is but one part of the heritage bequeathed to radio by telephony. Berliner invented and patented it for use in the ordinary telephone, where it soon became known, as it is to-day, as the transmitter. Technically, the microphone and the transmitter are identical. The "mike's" history and development, like that of the receiver, the amplifier and the vacuum tube, involved long and painstaking research before it was converted into the perfect instrument through which sound now spans the Atlantic and reverberates from end to end of the North American continent, not excepting even the frozen reaches of the Arctic.

Curious as it may seem, the highly efficient microphone used in broadcasting was developed long before its present use was anticipated. It was first utilized as a laboratory instrument in connection with researches conducted with transmitted speech. Speech, of course, is the product with which telephone engineers are most concerned. They experiment with it much as the chemist treats chemical compounds. It may be analyzed into its elements and each element studied by itself in order better to understand the conditions and requirements which telephone circuits must meet. In this "speech chemistry," it is necessary that the experimental

transmitter produce exact electrical copies of the
speech to be studied; therefore, a good transmitter
is an all-essential feature. When broadcasting
began, this "high quality" microphone was ready
for the new rôle.

To be capable of perfect reproduction the microphone must respond to high pitched tones and low
pitched tones equally. If any of the tones are either
over-emphasized or under-emphasized, an unnat-
uralness results. This is usually known as "distortion." Microphones are now built which respond
with great fidelity to all of the frequencies between
fifty and five thousand vibrations per second.

Naturally, because of the very severe requirements which it must meet, the broadcasting microphone is constructed somewhat differently from the
telephone transmitter. It consists of an "air-
damped" diaphragm on each side of which is located
a cup of carbon granules. The result is that during
operation the granules in one cup are compressed
and possess a low resistance, while those in the other
are released and possess a high resistance. Because of this double feature, the microphone is
sometimes referred to as the "push-pull" type. The
air damping supplies a very thin air cushion (about
one one-thousandth of an inch thick) which tends to
minimize any resonant effects that might otherwise
be present, due to the springiness of the diaphragm.

Not only must the microphone respond to a wide
range of frequencies faithfully, but it must repro-

duce a wide range of intensities. The same microphone that reproduces the grand crescendo of a whole orchestra may a moment later be required to reproduce the most delicate strains of a violin, which may scarcely be audible even to those in the same room. Indeed, the power represented by such sounds is barely a *millionth of a watt,* and the resulting motion of the diaphragm is too small to be detected. Experiments to develop the microphone were carried out in the Bell System's extensive laboratories which date back to the early Bell Company's experimental department started by Berliner and Watson in 1879.

All this explains why various means have to be used to encourage a speaker or singer to stand at the proper distance from the microphone—about four feet. Experience has shown that if a small rug is placed in front of the microphone pedestal, a speaker will unconsciously tend to confine himself to that region. Others do not feel oratorically at home unless they can walk around while talking, in which case provisions for long-distance speaking must be made. Temperamental radio performers accustomed to the bare floor of the stage have refused to sing while standing on plush carpet! In one instance, the program was delayed until boards could be brought in.

In 1873, James Clerk Maxwell, a profound English mathematician and apostle of Michael Faraday, published his classic *Electricity and Magnetism,* in which he boldly proclaimed the theory that electric waves could be reflected and refracted like light. He maintained that if the electrical wave motion with which Faraday experimented could be measured it, too, would be found to travel at the speed of one hundred and eighty-six thousand miles a second. The first man to demonstrate the correctness of Maxwell's theory, and to show that electric waves navigate the ether in the same manner as light waves, was Heinrich Hertz, a humble German professor at Bonn University. Hertz created in his laboratory electric sparks, or little flashes of artificial lightning. With their aid, he established that electric sparks cause electric waves in the ether precisely as sound causes acoustic waves in the air.

"Hertzian waves," as the astounded electrical world forthwith and thenceforward called the Bonn physicist's discovery, riveted scientists' attention in many lands. Branly, in France; Lodge, in England, and Popoff, in Russia, contributed substantially, by experiment and research, to the knowledge of "Hertzian waves." But to none of them did it occur that waves in the ether might be impressed into service for transmitting messages over immense distances. Years after radio communication was an accomplished fact, Sir Oliver Lodge wrote that he "did not realize that there would be a practical advantage in . . . telegraphing across space. . . . In this non-perception of the practical uses of wireless telegraphy, I undoubtedly erred."

It was reserved for William Marconi, twenty-two-year-old son of an Italian father and an Irish mother, to patent in 1896 a system of utilizing Hertzian waves for telegraphing through the air with the Morse key. "At the receiving station," writes Waldemar Kaempffert *(A Popular History of American Invention)*, "was the equally familiar receiving apparatus, in which a detector (the Branly-Lodge form of 'eye') was included. The Morse key was depressed. Sparks passed. They sent out waves into the ether. The key was released. The sparks and the waves ceased. Thus long or short trains of waves were sent out, corresponding with the dashes and dots of the Morse code. The receiver responded sympathetically. The eye or detector 'saw' while the key was down. It 'saw' nothing when the key was up. It received invisible telegraph flashes."

Thus was radio born.

By the end of 1897 Marconi was acclaimed the world round for the incredible feat of signaling nine or ten miles. "Half a mile was the wildest dream," said Sir William Preece, of the British Post-Office Department, when commenting upon the expectations of Marconi's more optimistic devotees.

Radio broadcasting, which is just another name for telephoning without wires, may be explained as follows:

If we throw a stone into a placid sheet of water, a series of ring-shaped waves is produced on the surface, stretching out in all directions until finally they become lost in the distance. An analogous action takes place when an electric spark rushes through the air. Forthwith electric waves radiate from the spark in all directions at a speed of about one hundred and eighty-six thousand miles a second.

There exist to-day other and more effective means in electrical science for producing thousands of these electric impulses in quick succession, so that we can produce such a stream of ether waves as to amount practically to a continuous ether wave current. If such a current, which may be called a "carrying current," is passed through one coil of a transformer before being thrown out into space at the broadcasting antenna, and then a speech wave current, produced by a microphone, is passed through the other coil of the same transformer, the electric speech vibrations will be impressed by induction, or electric influence, upon the carrying current. Then they will be taken along by the carrying current into space, to be picked up by the thousands of smaller antenna of the listeners-in with receiving apparatus. Thus, it is seen that the microphone is the means by which all sound to be broadcast is sent, and that the transformer is the apparatus which unites with that sound the energy by which that sound is carried an unlimited distance. *Both of these inventions, the microphone and the continuous current transformer used in radio broadcasting, were made by Emile Berliner in 1877.*

It is plain from this simplified explanation that in broadcasting, the speech current passes through the ether in all directions and *practically fills the ether of the whole world*. It can be caught up anywhere by receiving antenna, but before the now greatly enfeebled speech current can be made audible in the telephone receiver it has to be reinforced or amplified. This is accomplished by the well-known modern vacuum tube, or amplifier tube, invented by Lee De Forest, without which it would be practically impossible to listen to broadcasting over any great distance. De Forest's invention is one of the truly remarkable contributions to electricity and one of the greatest inventions of all time.

"Wired wireless" is the term applied where broadcast matter is sent part of the way over a long-distance telephone wire, to be tapped at any intermediate station and then sent or relayed through the ether. Wired wireless is the invention of Major-General George Owen Squier, U. S. A., retired, a friend and neighbor of Emile Berliner at Washington. For a number of years radio was beset with various exasperating difficulties. Broadcasting was largely confined to the winter season. It suffered from the now celebrated "static" and frequently from a sudden "fading out" of the voice or other broadcast sounds. It also was much more efficient at night than during daylight.

These and other atmospheric disorders were removed by "wired wireless." In General Squier's system the radio waves are guided along telegraph, telephone, or even electric light wires, and are not affected by ether disturbances in space. Arrived at a station, the reproductions are from there broadcast (relayed) for lesser distances over allotted ether wave lengths. "Wired wireless" has lifted radio from out of the depths of totally unreliable acoustic effects to the plane of an exact science. It lies at the bottom of the "hook up" system whereby radio to-day enjoys its fabulous radius of action.

What mighty strides has radio accomplished in the thirty years that have intervened since William Marconi, in 1896, achieved the miracle of communicating by wireless telegraphy over a distance of one and three-fourths miles! Amazing and revolutionary as have been the fruits of scientific invention, none rivals the romance of radio. In America the art has reached its highest development. Broadcasting has become as integral a part of the nation's daily life as telephoning and the newspapers. It is difficult to conceive what modern American existence would be without a receiving set, to be turned on and off like an electric light switch. Radio is to-day almost as indispensable to human intercourse in the United States as the automobile. Six million homes are estimated to be equipped with radio receivers, and the number is increasing every hour of each day. Already the percentage is nearly one set to every four homes. America has eighty per cent. of all the receiving sets in the world and five times as many broadcasting stations as all the rest of the countries put together.

Two thousand firms of radio manufacturers, one thousand firms of radio distributors and jobbers, and thirty thousand radio retail dealers comprise an industry which did two million dollars' worth of business in 1920; three hundred and fifty million dollars, in 1925, and probably will do four hundred million, or more, in 1926. Directly or indirectly employed in radio throughout the world is an army of two hundred and fifty thousand persons.

On January 1, 1922, there were but twenty-eight licensed broadcasting stations in the United States, the first one having received its authority to begin operations on September 15, 1921—one of the red-letter days of radio history. On May 29, 1926, there were five hundred and thirty-three licensed broadcasting stations. The number is limited only by the determination of the Department of Commerce, in the hands of which regulation of radio to the hour of this writing has been vested, to keep as clear as possible the ever-increasing traffic jam in the air. No new broadcasting licenses were issued by Secretary Hoover subsequent to November, 1925, although his department had on file, at the beginning of the summer of 1926, no fewer than six hundred and twenty-three applications for new licenses for stations in all parts of the United States.

On May 29, 1926, radio activities in the United States were officially tabulated as follows:

Class of Station	Number of Stations
Commercial Ship	1963
Commercial Land	323
Commercial Airplane	1
Technical and Training	35
Experimental	212
Government Ship	1214
Government Land	312
Government Airplane	4

On June 30, 1925, at the end of the last fiscal year of record, there were listed 15,111 amateur radio stations. The figures of ship stations are eloquent of the magical growth of radio. In 1909 the steamship *Republic* of the White Star Line met in collision the Italian ship *Florida* off Nantucket. The crash came in the middle of the night. The first call for help flashed from the ocean by a wireless operator thrilled the whole world. This was the immortal "C. Q. D." signal sent by Jack Binns, whose coolness and presence of mind resulted in saving the lives of one thousand, five hundred human beings on a sinking ship. It was the *Republic* disaster that focused the world's attention upon a struggling art and crystallized, in dramatic form, the priceless value of radio on shipboard. In a sense, radio has robbed the sea of its terrors. To-day all sea-going vessels carrying fifty persons or more are required by international law to carry radio installation and competent operators. In 1913 there were but

four hundred and seventy-nine American vessels
equipped with radio. In 1926, as the figures herein-
before set down indicate, three thousand, one hundred and seventy-seven American ships are fitted
with the most effective life-saving apparatus the
mind of man has yet devised.

Achievements in the broadcasting realm during
the past two or three years have piled up in an
unceasing crescendo of magnitude. Literally, no
one dares predict where they will end. Developments that seem fantastic to-day are altogether
likely to be recorded to-morrow. "Radio vision" is
believed to be just over the horizon. Transatlantic
radio-photograms burst upon the astounded gaze of
American and British newspaper readers, as a daily
feature, in the spring of 1926. Europe and the Amer-
icas exchange music and conversation by radio with
relative ease, though not, as yet, with that complete
accuracy or dependability which distinguish long-
distance transmission and reception between points
in the western hemisphere. On the north shore of
Long Island the Radio Corporation of America,
pioneer in transoceanic broadcasting, has constructed a "Radio Central"—a superpower radio
station for the simultaneous despatch of messages
to, and the receipt of messages from, countries
across the Atlantic. This colossus of radio, with its
steel towers covering more than ten square miles of
land, has made the United States the focal point
of the world in the transmission and reception of

wireless intelligence. It stands as a monument to American achievement, the greatest mile-stone in the progress of radio across the oceans. "Radio Central" was opened for public service on November 5, 1921, with a message to the world from the late President Harding. The message was received simultaneously and directly in twenty-eight different countries, including far-off New Zealand, Australia and the southermost republics of South America.

A year earlier, in November, 1920, radio was employed for the first time on a large scale as a means of broadcasting news of general interest. For that purpose the Westinghouse Company erected a broadcasting station KDKA at its great plant in East Pittsburgh and inaugurated the world's pioneer organized "radio program" service with the announcement of the Harding-Cox presidential election returns. Crude as that service was, compared with that rendered by the modern broadcasting station, it was a startling demonstration of the universal and beneficent power of radio. Little did the small groups of first listeners realize that within six years the all-penetrating voice of radio would echo into six million American homes.

Men and women differ as to what constitutes radio's outstanding achievement to date. There are several events that merit distinction and each was so marvelous that there is glory enough for all of them. When Firpo, the "wild bull of the pampas," knocked Jack Dempsey out of the ring at the Polo Grounds in New York City on September 14, 1923, the devastating punch from the Argentinian gladiator's glove was caught by the ringside microphone and heard a thousand miles away. Almost a year later to the day—on the memorable night of September 12, 1924—General John J. Pershing, about to retire from the generalship of the Armies of the United States, said good-by by radio, from his desk in the War Department, to the commanders of the nine corps areas of the country, stretching all the way from Governors Island in New York to the Presidio at San Francisco. It was not exactly a confidential farewell that Pershing took of his devoted subordinates, for the entire nation listened in, and enjoyed the General's half-bantering, half-sorrowing, parting confabs with his comrades precisely as if he were addressing every individual listener personally. It was a historic night, never to be forgotten by any one privileged to be part of it, as millions upon millions of the American people were.

Although Pershing was retiring from the army that night, the hook-up of the nation's broadcasting facilities on a continent-wide scale was designed primarily as part and parcel of the Defense Day test that day inaugurated. As explained to the millions of listeners by General J. J. Carty, one of the vice-presidents of the American Telephone and Telegraph Company, which was in charge of the mighty talkfest, its purpose was to illustrate in a practical manner the progress of communications. Mr. Carty said:

"The uses of radio in the national defense are many and one of its special functions is to carry to all of our citizens a national proclamation or call, or a message directed to the people at large. Omitting the great volume of messages carried daily over the telegraph wires, there passes each day over the telephone wires of the United States a grand total of fifty million messages. In handling this enormous volume of traffic, forty-five million miles of wire are in action, and their availability for service, should they be required in the national defense, has been demonstrated. This wire system is spread over our country like a great net covering the whole republic. From Washington direct connections may be established with more than twenty thousand central telephone offices, providing inter-communication between them and more than fifteen million individual telephone stations. Employed in this mighty inter-communication system throughout the United States are four hundred and twenty-five thousand men and women. This Defense Day test has demonstrated that they can be depended upon to perform any duty within their power that may devolve upon them at a moment of national emergency.

"In order that you of the air audience should hear the addresses broadcast this evening, nineteen radio stations have been called into service and thirty-eight thousand miles of wire are employed. From these radio stations the words are carried direct to your ears. It is possible to hold a conversation over the long distance telephone wires between Washington and any point in the United States. Because the radio stations are connected to the wires over which I am now talking, it is possible for all those who are listening by radio to hear the conversations.

"I will now call over the long distance wires a number of cities and towns extending from the Atlantic seaboard westward to the Pacific, placing all of them in direct wire communication with this room at Washington. To-night the radio stations are connected to these wires so the radio listeners may hear the conversations taking place over them. In the event of a national emergency, such messages would reach only the individuals for whom they were intended."

There is a plain-told tale worthy of the *Arabian Nights*. Such an achievement in communication was never before attempted in the history of the world. It was an epoch-making event.

The year 1924 was in countless directions an era of tremendous accomplishment in radio. Its high-water mark was the broadcasting of the Democratic "national confusion" in Madison Square Garden through those endless and bellicose days and nights of June and July. How many millions of edified, amused or horrified American citizens on that hectic occasion heard Alabama bellow, "twenty-four votes for Underwood," ballot after ballot; or listened in while Senator Thomas J. Walsh, the permanent and patient chairman of the bedlam, besought some delegate to "state his question"; or heard "Al" Smith's bands and boosters blare *The Sidewalks of New York*; or picked up, as millions did, every side remark uttered on the convention platform, even if it were only a stage whisper—how many of our people took part by radio in that unparalleled orgy of political turmoil will never be known. But it was

a prodigious event, the like of which humankind had
never known. There are cynics who avow that the
ability of the whole people to listen in while the
Democratic "national dissension" was in progress in
1924 was one of the reasons why its splendid nom-
inee, John W. Davis, was not elected.

In the ensuing national campaign radio's possibilities for political purposes were utilized to the
full. President Coolidge had no need, as his immediate predecessor had, to conduct a front-porch
campaign, or to swing around the circle and across
country as many predecessors had done. All Mr.
Coolidge had to do was to sit in his office or living-
room at the White House and broadcast his message
to the electorate, which he repeatedly did, while
millions listened in. The President does not shine
as a visible public speaker. But as a radio broadcaster he has taken his place among the immortals.
The Coolidge nasal twang "cuts through" the ether
ideally and makes the President a perfect performer
on the wave lengths. The night before election, in
1924, both the Republican and Democratic candidates sang their campaign swan songs by radio.
Mr. Coolidge was particularly effective. He was
also uncommonly human. "And now," he said, just
before closing, "I want to send a good-night greeting to my father, who is listening in at our old home
near Plymouth, Vermont." There are people who
say it was his economy program that swept Calvin
Coolidge into victory next day by a fabulous plu-

rality. That may be. But certain it is that the radio message to his father, since gathered to his progenitors, struck a responsive chord through the air audience across the country and made countless votes for the Republican ticket. Radio has never known a more kin-making touch of human nature. The Republican National Committee estimated that the President's final speech of the campaign by radio was delivered to an audience of over ten million people. In 1925, when Governor Smith was battling with the New York Legislature, he resorted to the radio as a means of bringing popular pressure to bear upon a hostile Assembly and Senate and succeeded in doing so. He broadcast an appeal to the people to write their representatives at Albany. They wrote, and "Al's" program went through.

The present writer, for the past three years, has been broadcasting regularly each week, except during the dull season at Washington, a review of national and international events known as *The Political Situation in Washington To-night* originally sent out from only station WRC of the Radio Corporation of America, it later was relayed through the super-power station of the same company, WJZ, at New York. Exactly how many millions of people listen to that weekly digest of the nation's business can not be guessed, except approximately. But the total runs into staggering figures. No one unprivileged to enjoy the unprecedented opportunity so generously offered, in the name of

Radio Central of the Radio Corporation of America on Long Island

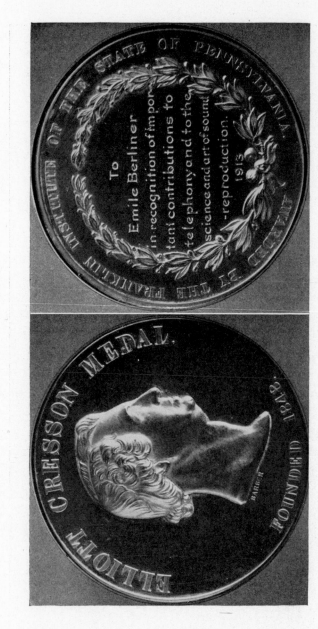

Elliott Cresson Gold Medal Given by the Franklin Institute to Emile Berliner in 1913

public service, by the Radio Corporation of America can comprehend the thrill it inspires every time the microphone at Washington is faced. One is certainly reaching a "circulation" outstripping many times the largest number of readers any newspaper reaches. It is not only a post of thrill. It is a station of responsibility. It carries voice and views into the White House and into the ears of members of the Cabinet, of Congress and of the diplomatic corps. It provokes a mountainous correspondence— the most instructive cross-section of popular opinion encountered in the broadcaster's quarter of a century of journalism. It has taught him the priceless value of objectivity and of understatement. It has sometimes made him wonder whether the communication of news and views one day may not become a regular function of the air rather than the monopoly of the press.

Two giants of radio—Herbert Hoover, Secretary of Commerce, to whose lot first fell the task of supervising broadcasting activities in the United States, and David Sarnoff, brilliant young vice-president and general manager of the Radio Corporation of America—have said terse and illuminating things about the magical public utility that is making the world over.

"Radio," says Hoover, "has already become so embedded in American life that we forget that the development of this great scientific discovery is but a little over five years old. I do not believe any other generation in history has had the privilege of witnessing the progress from birth to adolescence of an invention so profoundly affecting the social and economic life of the peoples of the world. No other discovery in all time invaded the home so rapidly and intrenched itself so securely as radio, and, though it is still far from maturity, we see great advances every year. . . . We have watched the industry grow from the curiosity of a scientific toy to a communication system now well-nigh universal. So great has it become in service that I believe it would be almost possible in a great emergency for the President of the United States to address an audience of forty or fifty millions of our people. It is bringing a vast amount of educational and informative material into the household. It is bringing about a better understanding among all of our people of the many problems that confront us. It is improving the public taste for music and entertainment. It is bringing contentment into the home. We are at the threshold of international exchange of ideas by direct speech. That will bring us better understanding of mutual world problems.

"Only over-optimistic prophets would attempt to predict radio advance. One thing we are sure of—that the radio industry is only in its youth, that it will continue to grow with increasing strength. If it will succeed, it must continue as in the past to devote itself to actual public service, to which it is already dedicated."

"Radio broadcasting," says Sarnoff, "is frequently characterized as the infant prodigy of the electrical family. But, as is often the case with a promising youngster, a little time and experience have already given it character and it is now making rapid strides toward maturity. Indeed, in its brief span of life, the radio industry has had the cleansing effect of several baptisms. Each time it emerged with a better understanding of its problems and those who have benefited by this experience gained more vigor and clearer vision.

"The year 1926 will, I believe, show the distinguishing marks of radio's efforts in the direction of stabilization. The public's preference in radio programs and radio devices is better understood. The problems of distribution are clarifying themselves, and the major problem of the business—broadcasting—is now receiving attention by many capable minds. The industry no longer has a place for the mere opportunist. Radio has become a permanent asset of our daily life and its future prosperity is assured."

In this wondrous story of the sky-rocket progress of radio, since Maxwell dreamed, Hertz materialized and Marconi achieved, Emile Berliner, inventor of the microphone and the continuous current transformer, played worthily and effectively his part. He is at the age, now, when men indulge in introspection, and in his reveries he speculates intensively about the spiritual value and ultimate potentialities of radio. Primarily he considers that it will become an irresistible force for peace. Men do not quarrel when they understand one another. Nations, Berliner thinks, are less likely to fling at one another's throats if they possess a common denominator in the field of thought interchange. Radio seems Heaven-sent, to the originator of the microphone, for the purpose of establishing upon earth for all time and among all peoples the reign of good will.

CHAPTER XXVI

EMILE BERLINER TO-DAY

AUGUST THYSSEN—"King Thyssen," the Rhinelanders used to call the late colossus of German steel and iron—had a philosophy which he epitomized in the phrase: "If I rest, I rust." That terse and alliterative expression of the strenuous life personifies Emile Berliner. His entire career has been one long consistent refusal to rust, and to-day, just over the threshold of his threescore years and fifteen, he as resolutely eschews the privilege of rest. An uncommonly sturdy physique, a mental attitude toward men and matters that defies the ravages of time, and an unquenchable sense of humor combine to fit him, at seventy-five, for new attempts at conquests in whichever fields of scientific or humanitarian endeavor he cares to furrow.

His hand, indeed, is actually on a plow that he expects to trench entirely new ground in the area of architecture. As it was acoustics that led Berliner into the unexplored regions of the telephone and the talking machine, it is the science of sound that has again summoned him to active service on the firing-line of invention. Emile Berliner, at the

beginning of the autumn of 1926, is ready to introduce a scientifically worked-out method of making
churches, theaters, opera-houses and assembly halls
of every description acoustically infallible.

He contends that there has never been a time
when architects could guarantee satisfactory acoustic qualities in any interior designed for auditory
purposes—whether it be a church, a cathedral, a
concert hall, a railroad waiting-room (in which train
departures or arrivals are announced), a theater,
or a full-sized auditorium in which great gatherings
like national conventions are held. The reason why
poor acoustics can not be combatted with mathematical precision has never been positively known.
The usual recourse, when an interior is found to be
acoustically defective, is to cover the walls with
sound absorbing material. This weakens the objectionable reverberations or other acoustic impurities,
but also reduces the loudness of the sounds sent
forth by speaker, singer, actor, instrumentalist or
orchestra. Moreover, porous walls covered with
cloth or felt are highly insanitary, absorb dust and
germs, and can not be washed, as walls of public
halls require to be, at frequent intervals.

Berliner studied hall acoustics for years. He
is an inveterate theater-goer and music-lover, and
a sharply-trained ear long since made him acute in
the detection of acoustical inadequacies in many of
the temples of entertainment into which the American public is from time to time beguiled. Berliner

eventually came to the conclusion that the cause of bad acoustics is the hardness or rigidity of the usual brick or stone walls. He observed that an auditorium that has wooden walls, especially of pine or spruce that vibrates freely, also has superior acoustics. It was this theory that Berliner developed logically in what he terms "acoustic tiles." These are composed of porous cement, are as hard as stone, and yet have the resonance of wood when vibrated by a tuning fork. They are the fruit of more than twenty years of research and experiment.

Emile Berliner's remedy for the knotty problem of hall acoustics consists of a process of cementing these tiles to the walls of an auditorium over a sufficiently large area, thus combining the hardness and dignity of a stone wall with the resonance of wooden panels. The tiles can be molded ornamentally to please the taste of an architect, or builder, or property-owner, and may form the final finish of walls. They may even be painted without reducing their acoustic efficiency.

Another method which Berliner has found to be feasible is to attach flat acoustic cells of wire netting to a rough finished wall and spread "acoustic cement" over them. This the inventor has demonstrated to be thoroughly efficient, acoustically, and the process lends itself to any treatment applicable to plain cement walls.

A prominent Roman Catholic churchman, before whom Berliner demonstrated his invention, repre-

sented that in countless communities Catholic
churches have been erected with an eye to nearly
everything except proper hearing facilities. He
was fascinated by the prospect that Berliner's
acoustic tiles offer and expressed the belief that the
princes of the Roman church, then about to assemble
at Chicago for the great twenty-eighth International
Eucharistic Congress, would be deeply interested in
the possibility of enabling a priest, bishop or car-
dinal to celebrate mass in speaking tones and yet
be audible many hundreds of feet away. That is the
boon Berliner believes his acoustic tiles hold out.
Architects and builders who have heard him ex-
pound his theories are persuaded they contain germs
of an important advance in interior construction.

Berliner has converted the basement of his
"Bureau of Health Education" building on Columbia Road in Washington into a laboratory for conducting practical experiments with acoustic tiles.
Ordinarily the room in question serves the purpose
of a billiard room. Berliner has covered the walls
with his "loud speaking" tiles. A simple experiment which he is fond of making is to let a visitor
walk a little distance from the door in the hall that
leads into the billiard room. Then Berliner asks
the visitor to listen to his own footsteps. As soon
as the billiard room is entered, the footsteps sound
twice or three times as loud as they sounded in the
hall outside, although the floors of the hall and the
billiard room are of precisely the same material.

Another demonstration that carries simple conviction to the lay mind is for Berliner to lead a caller to a brick wall, and there set a tuning fork to vibrating. The fork is applied to the wall, but scarcely any sound is heard. Then the inventor lays against the brick wall one of his tiles measuring about eight inches in diameter and three-eighths of an inch in thickness and touches the vibrative fork against the face of the tile. There results a ringing sound as if the tuning fork were applied to the sound board of a piano.

Berliner asserts there is nothing in the science of acoustics that challenges the soundness of his premises or the practical form which he has given them. He has boldly disregarded previous theories, and, as an irrepressible scientific iconoclast, has set out on wholly original paths to achieve a solution. One major demonstration on a large scale—say, correcting with the use of his tiles the notoriously bad acoustics in some well-known church or theater— will, Berliner is confident, establish the practical utility of his invention. He holds that the prevalence of improper hearing facilities in public places without number the world over is due to imperfect reasoning on the part of architect and builder and to the chance they are given to taking—of "guessing right." Acoustic tiles are designed to substitute reliability for guess-work. Said an architect to Berliner on one occasion: "Acoustics has always been a gamble." Berliner rejoined: "You're right; and, as I'm against all gambling, I want to stop this!"

Berliner made the first public presentation of his solution for coming to grips with the obscure and baffling problem of hall acoustics in Washington on October 8, 1925. The occasion was a meeting of the local chapter of the American Institute of Architects. In that presence Berliner read the following paper:

"The object of this paper is to present to you the solution of a problem that has at all times appeared a difficult one to handle.

"Let me first advance the following propositions:

"1. Every partly or nearly wholly enclosed body of air assumes a rhythmic vibration which will resound either as a tone or as a so-called reverberation whenever that air-body is agitated; the larger the volume of air, the slower the rhythm of the tone or of the reverberation will be.

"2. When the agitation is caused by any sound in the neighborhood of the air-body whose vibration corresponds with the individual rhythm of the air-body, then the response will be strong and resonant.

"3. When the agitation is caused by a sound whose pitch is merely acoustically related to the rhythm of the air-body, then the resonance or the reverberation will be only noticeable.

"4. The harder or the more rigid the walls which enclose an air-body, the more intense will be its individual tone or its reverberation.

"In collections of physical apparatus we often

see sets of resonators consisting of hollow brass balls of different sizes which are provided with open necks like a bottle and each of which will reverberate and emit its own resonant tone when that same note is sounded in the neighborhood, or when air is blown across the open neck.

"Organ pipes are examples of such resonators and when made of metal the sound emitted by them is louder, though sometimes less penetrating or carrying, than if made of wood.

"Any bottle will illustrate all this by sounding or singing notes of different pitches into or in front of it or blowing air across the open neck when the individual note can be quickly discovered. I have here a set of dinner gongs consisting of metal bars mounted over wooden boxes that have openings at the tops and which are tuned to correspond with the notes of the bars. When the holes in the boxes are covered and the bars are struck they emit their notes but feebly and without resonance. But when the boxes are open the latter will sound in unison when the bars are struck and the notes will be ringing with a beautiful resonance.

"The pitch of every sound depends on the number of its vibrations, and the limits within which the human ear can differentiate between different pitches range from about sixteen vibrations per second for the lowest notes to about sixteen thousand per second for the highest. Below sixteen vibrations the sounds are mere noises or booms and above about sixteen thousand they appear as squeaks or high whistles if emitted by instruments. While, however, the average human ear can differentiate sounds only within about these limitations, the sounds beyond, either below sixteen thousand or above sixteen thousand, maintain the law of resonance. This is particularly obvious with low pitched sounds which will become audible if, for instance, octaves of their notes are sounded in their neighborhood. We may even assume that large masses of enclosed air might represent individual notes having only a few vibrations per second, and yet such air-bodies would emit their rhythmic sound if they were agitated by sounds whose notes may be related and are, say, one or more octaves above them. Nor would this be necessary if such air-bodies were agitated by mere shocks. A blow by a hammer, a tramp of feet, or a striking of any hard object will set up the resonance and produce the individual vibration of that air-body, though this note may be of a pitch below the recognizable register of the human ear. It is then termed reverberation pure and simple.

"The resonators mentioned heretofore, like organ pipes or dinner gongs, were all of regular forms, being either tubes or oblong boxes. But we have in the string instruments of the violin type hollow boxes of irregular shapes which apparently do not follow out the propositions advanced. If they did, then every time a string note was played which corresponded to the individual note of the air-body that note would be reenforced by the violin box and would sound much louder than the rest. On first consideration it might be concluded that the irregular shape of the violin or the bass viol was responsible for the absence of individual resonance or reverberation. This is, however, erroneous, because a violin made of glass or metal, such as now and then has been tried, does emit its individual note and follows our fourth proposition relating to the question of how rigid the walls are which enclose the air-body. The note so emitted by a glass or metal violin of a Stradivarius model corresponds to a tone having about five hundred vibrations per second or to the tone of B of the middle tenor register.

"Hence it follows that the reason why a violin does not resonate or reverberate the individual tone of its enclosed air-body is because its walls are not rigid enough to permit the development of individual resonance.

"I will now present some facts which, while observed in an entirely different branch of technology, have considerable bearing on the problem of hall acoustics. Many years ago when I began my investigations which led up to the gramophone, I was bothered considerably by the resonance of the horns which I used as sound collectors. Individual notes would be recorded and would reproduce much louder than other notes by the same singer or from the same musical instrument.

"I soon discovered that the disturbing sounds were always in the same key and that their notes corresponded to the individual note of the horn used for recording them. These horns were at that time usually several feet long and had flared openings, or so-called bells, from eight to twelve inches in diameter. Their individual note was well within the register of the male voice so that scarcely a song or a musical composition could be recorded but the disturbance took place. Soprano voices were not so much affected by it, but the instruments used for accompanying the voice were. Employing smaller horns, while doing away with the disturbance, reduced the sensitiveness of the contrivance and, since loud effects were desired, singers would have to stand close to the horn in order to register their voices with sufficient power or amplitude.

"I do not recall now what else I did to try to remedy the trouble, but I finally discovered that punching a certain number of small holes into the sides of the horn would destroy the individual resonance of the horns and obviate the disturbance.

"The modus operandi consisted in punching three or four rows of small holes, each row of about six holes, lengthwise, along the horn into the material of which the horn was made, generally common tinplate. This would much reduce the individual resonance. Then holes would be gradually added, the resonance tried again until it would have ceased. After this point was reached the effect of adding further holes would merely weaken the capacity of the horn for transmitting or deflecting sound against the recording diaphragm.

"Such perforated, or as we used to call them, ventilated horns faithfully transmitted all sounds equally well to the recording diaphragm and permitted perfect recording, and with all larger horns perforations have been employed ever since.

"But when horns of these sizes were employed in reproducing machines the disturbance of individual resonance was not noticed because the pressure of the sound vibrations came from the diaphragm outward and the cause of the resonance which is rhythmic elastic compression of enclosed air did not occur.

"When about twenty years ago I prepared this address originally, it occurred to me that the theories of individual resonance as advanced in the four propositions with which I began this paper might be further tested if I tried horns of pyramidical instead of conical shape such as are used in cabinet talking machines. In such horns there are four triangular plates of wood or metal which form a sound chamber. Their sides are not rigid as in a conical horn, but semi-elastic, each side forming a panel capable of freely vibrating within certain limits, depending on the thickness of the wood or other material of which they consisted.

"My anticipations that such a horn would exhibit reduced individual resonance in recording, or none at all, proved true and confirms the fourth proposition that individual resonance or reverberation of enclosed air-bodies depends on the greater or lesser rigidity of the walls which enclose the air.

"Let me now take a brief survey of what we find in large rooms, halls or auditoriums, considering their acoustic conditions.

"What is demanded is that sounds from the platform of the speaker or singer or performer should be heard loudly and distinctly over all the auditorium. In particular boomy reverberations should be absent, because they not only impair distinctness, but jumble and destroy the evenness of rendition so that some portions of a speech are heard distinctly and others not.

"It is an old experience that a hall when empty may exhibit marked reverberation but, after the audience has filed in, the disturbance has disappeared; at the same time, however, the resonance of the sound of the speaker or performer is greatly weakened. What has happened is this. The side of the auditorium taken by the acoustically elastic wooden floor has been covered with a mass of flesh and clothing which absorb the vibrations striking against them and therefore impair the resonance of the voices or notes themselves.

"Or an empty and unfinished room may exhibit a fine natural resonance without any disturbing reverberation, but after it has been carpeted, and hangings put in, sounds are muffled. This accounts for the fact that a piano or a violin tried out in the bare and unfurnished rooms at the music dealers and appearing of brilliant tone will often sound unsatisfactory when it is being played in the furnished home of the purchaser.

"The worst examples of bad acoustics occur in fine old cathedrals and in the large waiting-rooms of magnificent railroad stations. It is next to impossible to understand the sermons or the strenuous efforts of the criers when calling out trains. There are larger churches built of brick or stone in which the acoustics are not so very bad, but very few in which they are very good. At best it requires careful voice handling on the part of the minister, unless he be a natural elocutionist, to make himself easily understood. When a newly built hall is found to have poor acoustics the remedies applied, while helping in some respects, usually impair the speaking voice trying to reach the distant part of the audience as well.

"But there are within my knowledge two large auditoriums the acoustic properties of which are not only not bad but exceptionally fine, and these are the Tabernacle at Salt Lake City, seating eight thousand people, and the Wagner Theater in Bayreuth, with a seating capacity of about two thousand.

"I shall never forget the impression which I received when our traveling party one summer day inspected the Bayreuth Theater at a time when no performances were given. After we had entered I began to comment on the seating capacity and the simplicity of the designs. Every word I uttered in a subdued voice echoed into my ears with wonderful resonance. It was not the boomy reverberation one notices in cathedrals but a true resonance which increased the volume of the voice without in the slightest degree changing its quality. And no matter in what part of the theater I tried it the resonance was beautiful and perfect everywhere.

"In the very large auditorium at Salt Lake City words spoken in an ordinary voice at the speaker's platform are distinctly understood at distant places, and of course the musical results are always superb.

"Both these great halls are built of wood, or their interiors at least show wooden walls, and in the light of my fourth proposition it leads to the conclusion that the elastic or vibratory character of wooden auditorium walls is mostly responsible for their good acoustical results.

"There are, however, several objections to the using of wooden walls in large halls or auditoriums. They are inflammable and they lack architectural dignity. They do not impress with that feeling of permanence which stone or marble walls, or cement imitations of these, convey to the discerning mind.

"In the new development which I bring before you to-day a compromise has been effected by *covering walls with elastic cement tiles* and which have the acoustic resonance of wood. This is accomplished, first, by mixing a porous material like asbestos, pumice or sawdust with the cement, and second, by shaping these tiles so that when joined to the wall they form vibratory diaphragms. At present the acoustic tiles are eight inches in diameter and consist of square center portions about a quarter-inch thick and projecting rims by which they are cemented to the wall. With substances like asbestos and pumice the tiles could be made of china clay or of terra cotta and be baked in fire as a real tile is.

"Acoustic tiles may have any surface grain desired and it is not unlikely that grouping together larger and smaller tiles on the same set of walls may result in increased resonance for certain definite purposes.

"Existing churches, theaters or concert halls with defective acoustics may, I think, be readily corrected by covering sections of their interiors with acoustic tiles to a sufficient height for catching and reflecting the voices of speakers or singers as well as the tones of instruments."

CHAPTER XXVII

AN INVENTOR'S HUMAN SIDE

X-RAYING the man to-day, at threescore and fifteen, with so many achievements to his credit that almost any one of them would assure him place in the Hall of Fame, it is plain that inventive success came to Emile Berliner because of three qualities indispensable in the scientific explorer—driving force, inconquerable optimism and contempt for failure. Berliner is a stubborn man, and stubbornness, in an inventor, is pure gold.

"Above all," he once said, "the inventor must have the patience and fortitude to face failures—hundreds of them, if necessary—and still keep on. He must be ready to average ninety-nine failures for one success or one encouraging development. He must work hard, and be content to slave for months at a time without registering apparent progress. He must not be disheartened by the necessity to travel over the same ground again and again, or by the sudden necessity to detour. Therein lies the key to victory—never-ending application. The idea that an inventor is necessarily a genius is entirely fallacious. Genius for invention is only the capacity for

concentration. Given that, plus the power of observation, and you have the raw material for a successful inventor.''

Berliner has frittered away an amazingly small
amount of time on the trifles of modern existence.
He tabulates work as his recreation, though he confesses to one play-time hobby—billiards. He attributes to the creative atmosphere of America his
passion for accomplishing things. "In the United
States," Berliner says, "you *are* what you have
done." He considers that he was richly blessed in
having been deprived of too many advantages in
early life. "I once knew a man," the inventor likes
to recall, "who said he gave his son every possible
advantage except one—he could not give him a poor
father."

Intellectual curiosity was implanted in Berliner
in youth. At the only school he ever attended, Wolfenbüttel, in Hanover province, which he left when
he was fourteen years old, his teachers dubbed him
a hermit "because I was so much alone—thinking."
All his life he has cultivated the tedious art of taking pains. He has a card-index mind which endows
him with a talent for sorting out ideas and for
winnowing theoretical chaff from practical grain.
He possesses an extraordinarily concentrated eyesight—a physical vision which supplements a mental insight and forms a combination making for
unusual power of penetration. Unlike most inventors, Berliner is an able business man. He made

shrewd investments, largely in District of Columbia land, with the early fruits of his scientific successes. He has always preferred looking after his own affairs, and has a passion for promptness and orderliness in connection with them.

Asked to name Emile Berliner's principal personal characteristic, the average man or woman who knows him unhesitatingly says: "Generosity." A fortune came to him relatively soon in life, and it grew rapidly. His benefactions have always kept pace with his prosperity, though they were not, and are not, of the sort that attract the light of publicity. Berliner has devoted a king's ransom to his child health work.

Berliner bubbles with good nature. He would rather perpetrate a witticism than an opinion, and prefers telling or hearing good stories to holding post-mortems on his scientific past. To many an aspiring young man Berliner has said: "Never dwell on a success. Reach out for the next!" He is a modest man. For more than ten years family and friends tried in vain to induce him to compile his autobiography. He thinks autobiography is the stage of life a man reaches when he begins to take himself seriously, and Berliner has always warded off that symptom of dotage, as he calls it. Within these pages is the only account of the inventor's career for which Berliner has ever taken the time to assemble essential data. When friends become adulatory about his discoveries, he dismisses these as "just good guesses." He wanted to call this volume *Guessing Right*. Berliner tenaciously refused to become the lion of festivities which prominent Washington friends wanted to arrange in honor of the seventy-fifth anniversary of his birth on May 20, 1926. When the day came, he stole away to Swarthmore College, where a favorite granddaughter, Miss Gertrude Sanders, is an undergraduate, and spent the diamond jubilee with her and nine other co-eds at lunch and on the Quaker campus.

Once Berliner met an old friend in a Washington optician's shop after a lapse of many years. He banteringly berated the man for "neglecting" him and never taking the trouble to reknit the ties of other times. The friend, a little flustered, resorted to the ruse of changing the conversation by admiring a beautiful pigeon-blood ruby ring which Berliner wore. "Emile," he said, "that's a handsome ring you've got there. You promised me that!" Berliner replied that he was sorry he couldn't part with the jewel, as it was a present, many years previous, from Mrs. Berliner. A couple of days later the inventor's old friend was astonished to receive from a fashionable jeweler's shop an exact duplicate of the ruby ring with Berliner's compliments.

When Berliner was launching his pure-milk crusade in Washington, he was at more or less incessant war with the local doctors. The Medical Society objected in particular to his gratis circulation of *The Bottle-Fed Baby*, on the ground that it

MR. BERLINER IN FRONT OF MICROPHONE AT WRC BROADCASTING
STATION, WASHINGTON, D. C. THE AUTHOR OF THIS VOLUME SINCE
1923 HAS BROADCAST "THE POLITICAL SITUATION IN WASHINGTON
TO-NIGHT" WEEKLY THROUGH THE MICROPHONE HERE SHOWN

MR. BERLINER AMONG CHILDREN OF PUBLIC HEALTH CLASS WHICH CONTAINS PUPILS
IN THE EARLY STAGE OF TUBERCULOSIS. *Inset:* DR. GEORGE M. KOBER

gave young mothers so much and so sound advice on the rearing of infants that it was almost as potent as an apple a day—it kept the doctor away. Finally the Medical Society decided to invite Berliner to a joint conference at which the merits and demerits of *The Bottle-Fed Baby* would be thoroughly discussed.

"We shall name five delegates," said the medics to Berliner, "and you may name five."

"I don't need but three," the inventor-humanitarian rejoined.

The conference was duly convened. Berliner's trio of protagonists consisted of Doctor George Martin Kober, Professor of Hygiene and Dean of the Medical Faculty of Georgetown University, Washington; Doctor Ernest Charles Schroeder, Veterinarian and Expert on Animal Industry in the Department of Agriculture; and Mrs. E. R. Grant, Chairman of the Advisory Committee on Child Health Education of the National Tuberculosis Association.

Berliner introduced his "big three" to the Medical Society "trial board" and reeled off their respective ranks, titles and scientific stations in life with impressive solemnity.

Going through the motions of being staggered by this galaxy of talent, the spokesman of the doctors ejaculated:

"Why, Mr. Berliner, you leave me speechless!"

"Well, Doctor," Berliner replied, "we expected to render you speechless with our argument, but not with our mere presence. Are we to consider the matter settled without conference?"

When the World War broke out in 1914, Emile Berliner, though of German origin, made prompt avowal of his unqualified pro-Ally sympathies. He has always had an amused contempt for the pretensions of the more arrogant type of German, especially of the titled aristocrat and military breed. Menials in Germany, when they want to fawn upon a superior, frequently address a vain and susceptible male as "Herr Baron" (Mr. Baron). To-day Emile Berliner is fond of bestowing that mock title of nobility upon his intimate friends, especially if they understand German.

The inventor of the microphone, despite his German blood, is a tireless spinner of yarns illustrative of Teuton pretensions and foibles.

"A Yankee millionaire once was motoring through Berlin," Berliner narrates, "and drove helter-skelter through Brandenburg Gate (Berlin's Arc de Triomphe at the head of Unter den Linden). A policeman stopped the American on the other side of the gate. 'You're fined five hundred marks,' the cop said. 'What for?' asked the Yankee. 'For using a part of this arch reserved exclusively for the kaiser.' The American pulled out his pocketbook and gave the policeman one thousand marks. 'I said five hundred marks,' the *Schutzmann* explained. 'I heard you the first time,' the man from the United States said, 'but I'm coming back!'"

Berliner was once asked what impressed him most about pre-war Berlin, when sabers rattled more conspicuously than in this democratic day on the Spree. "The Prussian mounted police," he replied. "I liked the intelligent look on the face of the horses!" The republican police has improved.

A friend, during this golden jubilee year of the invention of the Bell telephone, asked Emile Berliner if he thought the telephone is now perfect.

"No," the maker of the transmitter chuckled. "I've got three more inventions up my sleeve—one is a scheme to prevent your getting the wrong number; another, which'll prevent you from being cut off, and a third, perhaps the most important of all, which will prevent johnnies and flappers from talking at a stretch more than twenty minutes during the busy hours of the forenoon!"

Berliner says he has only one regret about the invention of the gramophone. He thinks it ought to have been devised so that records couldn't be played after ten o'clock at night, except for dancing.

In his old home on Columbia Road, in Washington, Berliner once had a large golden eagle hanging in the front hall. A gullible visitor was inquisitive about the gleaming bird's origin.

"That," said Berliner, with great gravity, "is the original American eagle shot by George Washington in the Rocky Mountains. He gave it to his bodyguard, who was a cousin of Uncle Tom, and for years it hung in Uncle Tom's cabin. One day Har-

riet Beecher Stowe visited Uncle Tom, and out of
gratitude for having been written up by Mrs. Stowe,
he gave her the eagle. Mrs. Stowe took it to New
York and after her death her effects were sold at
auction. It was bought by a wholesale feather merchant, and one day I bought it from him!''

Berliner has an uncommonly good memory—better, he says, than the absent-minded German professor who said: ''There are three things I can
never remember: names, faces, and the other thing
I have completely forgotten!''

Although he has been away from the Fatherland
fifty-six years, Berliner still speaks a classic German, and can quote Goethe and Schiller like a *Herr
Professor*. When the war depopularized the use of
the kaiser's jawbreaking language in America, a
German-American friend asked Berliner what the
latter was going to substitute for *Gesundheit*
(Health), the ancient German greeting when one
hears another sneeze.

''Say 'Liberty!' '' Berliner suggested. He acted
on his own proposal, and throughout the war when
anybody in the Berliner household sneezed, somebody exclaimed: ''Liberty!''

Berliner considered Luther Burbank one of the
outstanding men of our day. Once the inventor of
the microphone described the union of a certain
eminent American couple, the fairer of whom is in-
incomparably more charming, as ''a Luther Burbank
marriage—the union of a 'lemon' and a 'peach.' ''

Hardly a day passes that Emile Berliner is not asked his recipe for keeping eternally youthful in spirit and point of view, looking young out of tune with his age, and for the almost boyish springiness that marks his every step and gesture. He claims never to have sipped at the rejuvenating fountain of Ponce de Leon, or had resort to any of the standard elixirs of life, but to have adhered, rather, to six whimsical "rules" of his own fashioning:

1. Select healthy parents.
2. Follow Doctor Pat's advice to his friend Mike: "Nivver have anything on yer mind but yer hat."
3. Keep away from raw milk, from raw cream and from butter made of unpasteurized cream.
4. Get all the sleep your body seems to need.
5. Seek the association of persons younger than yourself.
6. Don't carry grievances—cultivate cheerfulness, kindliness and smiles.

Because like "Bobs" in Rudyard Kipling's barrack-room ballad, " 'e does not advertise," Emile Berliner's virtues as father, friend and man are those most often acclaimed in the immediate circle of his acquaintances and admirers. They know of the love he has lavished upon a large family; of the pious devotion with which he honors the memory of his mother; of the unostentatious and unrecorded charities he is constantly rendering; of his aggressive public spirit; of his fondness for old friends, especially the comrades of his struggling days.

They know, in particular, of the sympathetic background and sustaining influence which have been vouchsafed Emile Berliner by a well-regulated home, over which the companion of forty-five years still presides. They know what the combination of wife and fireside has meant to the restless inventor. They know the joyous pride he has unceasingly taken in the six children that Cora Adler Berliner bore him—all of them now grown up and married, with a glorious brood of seven grandchildren in whose company Emile Berliner derives endless confirmation of his theory that advancing age is most successfully resisted amid the environment of "flaming youth."

CHAPTER XXVIII

EMILE BERLINER does not believe that we already inhabit the best of all possible worlds. He has survived to see it become an immeasurably happier place of abode, spiritually, esthetically and scientifically, than any planet the ancients could possibly have envisaged. In that development of human well-being, Berliner has had a share, as these pages have set out. But the inventor-humanitarian, whose optimism and idealism are always tinctured with realism and common sense, has an abiding faith that if he could survey the terrestrial scene a hundred years hence, he would find mankind as far in advance of present-hour progress as the America of to-day fabulously outstrips the pioneer era from which it sprang.

Yet, paradoxical as it may sound, Emile Berliner's firmest conclusion with reference to the future is: *"I do not know."* He contends that "we know only so far as we can demonstrate." He points out that those who have demonstrated most feel, as a rule, that they have not penetrated very far; that, in a sense they have only scratched the surface of the inscrutable soil they essayed to till. Berliner, in a word, holds that the true scientist is, intuitively, the least dogmatic of men. The word cocksureness is not in his lexicon.

When Berliner is asked for his "philosophy of life," as he frequently is, he takes recourse in James Clerk Maxwell's *Atoms*. In that essay, the English mathematician who blazed the trail that led to radio, said:

"Science is incompetent to reason upon the creation of matter itself out of nothing. We have reached the utmost limit of our thinking faculties when we have admitted that, because matter can not be eternal and self-existent, it must have been created."

"Whenever I scan that prescient passage in Maxwell," says Berliner, "and realize that the greatest mathematical physicist of the nineteenth century thus had to admit the fallibility of human logic, I cease to worry about the infinite." Berliner has a personal creed that is based to a considerable extent on the Maxwellian theory. As to religion, Berliner inclines to Elbert Hubbard's view that "mere dogma is a hard substance that forms in a soft brain."

But the maker of the microphone believes that religion is an indispensable factor in life because its institutional feature—the church—is the only agency that has for its primary object the presentation and propagation of ideals. Without ideals,

Berliner asserts, "civilized society would disintegrate."

One of the calls echoing urgently from the future to the present, in Emile Berliner's judgment, is for a program of popular education in sex psychology, i. e., the understanding, by men, of the minds of women. He considers such a program fundamental to the happiness of the human race. If the sexes understood each other better, greater unity of purpose would come out of willing compromises, and marriage would be less of a gamble.

"Marriage," Berliner affirms, "is a mutual accommodation between the natural instinct to mate and the laws of society that are necessary for the protection of children. Happy marriages are undoubtedly the best solutions of the mating instinct and afford the most solid foundation for civilized society. Unfortunately, economic conditions continuously operate against early marriages craved by Nature. Human society, of course, has been grappling with the problem, in all its multifarious ramifications, since the dawn of Time, and demanded a solution not yet vouchsafed the children of men. Only in recent times has youth apparently revolted openly against a system it finds intolerable, claiming the right to love as youth's natural prerogative."

"What is your remedy for this state of affairs?" Berliner was asked while this story of his life was in the making.

"Probably Ingersoll had the right answer," Berliner replied. "Many years ago I discussed this riddle of the universe—sex—with the great agnostic. Ingersoll said: 'Some day you scientific men will furnish a simple means of birth control. That will help to bring about a solution of the sex question.' Ingersoll placed his finger on the strategic feature of the problem. To-day the time which he foresaw has almost arrived."

On the eternal issue of how a world peopled with men and women, in whom belligerency and covetousness are dormant, if not active, traits, can abolish war, Emile Berliner holds stimulating views. He believes the international millennium is much more likely to be promoted by language than by leagues. "A prime means to 'end war,' " he says, "would in my opinion be the adoption of a universal language which every schoolchild in creation would learn. Literature in that language would then be fostered in every land. Radio would speak a tongue understood around the globe, and could carry it to the uttermost corners. I believe that English, with reformed and simplified spelling, would make an excellent universal language. This would lead the nations readily into a common channel of thought, would make every mind accessible to universal ideals, and would enable every great writer to disseminate his ideals in all directions. The fraternization of the nations would automatically ensue and continue. There would be no more 'foreigners' or 'aliens' in a world inhabited by men and women who talked to each other in a language common to all.''

Berliner contends that such thoughts as these are not the dreamings of an impractical idealist. "On March 23, 1926," he points out, "the *Associated Press* carried the following striking news: 'Complete annihilation of space for the human voice is the ultimate aim of engineers of the American Telephone and Telegraph Company, now perfecting a commercial transatlantic telephone service. They believe that ultimately men will be able to talk between any two points on the face of the earth.' Thus, we see, the engineers are doing their part. Let the dreamers and the idealists—and the philologists—now do theirs.''

His contemporaries often seek light and leading from Emile Berliner on the puzzle of the life hereafter. "Intermolecular space," he replies, "exists between the molecules or atoms and may partake and embody in its ether something of the activities of the molecules. Under this entirely scientific assumption a so-called astral body, a body of ether, might remain after the dissolution or scattering of the molecules of the human body. This, I believe, as a theory, might presage some individual activity after death.''

Emile Berliner, as he looks down the endless corridor of the future, foresees a world in which women through educated motherhood will play a tremendously increasing rôle. In his own realm of science, in particular, he visualizes them as factors bound one day to serve mankind as effectually as men scientists in the long past have done. That women, with rare exceptions like Madame Curie, hitherto have not shone scientifically Berliner attributes primarily to their lack of educational opportunity, rather than to inherent incapacity. Actuated by that conviction Berliner in 1908, with the cooperation of the American Association of University Women, founded "The Sarah Berliner Research Fellowship." It was established in memory of the inventor's mother, a woman of parts, who, of course, had not had a college education herself—women in those days, neither in Germany nor in America, even having been admitted to university courses— but a woman who was decidedly intellectual in her interests.

It was largely at the instigation of Mrs. Christine Ladd Franklin, wife of Fabian Franklin, and one of the first women to complete the work required for the doctor's degree at Johns Hopkins University, that Emile Berliner was induced to found the Fellowship. It is open to all American women holding the degree of Doctor of Philosophy or Doctor of Science, who give promise of distinction in the subject to which they are devoting themselves. The Fellowship is available for research in physics, chemistry or biology. The committee on fellowships of the Association of University Women is the committee on awards. The university women in charge of the Sarah Berliner Fund give explicit recognition to those candidates for the award, who can carry on research and at the same time might have the privilege of giving one or more courses of lectures at some university or other institution of learning. The value of the Fellowship is more than twelve hundred dollars a year.

Professor Agnes L. Rogers, of the department of education at Bryn Mawr College, who is now chairman of the Committee on Fellowships of the American Association of University Women, says:

"Mr. Berliner's foundation was one of the first, if not the first, fellowships for women in the United States and the very first designated for work in science. As it has always been the largest fellowship for women in this country until 1926, when the Guggenheim Fellowships were founded, amounting to twenty-five hundred dollars each, the women who have held the Berliner Fellowship have been very distinguished. It has bound to our Association of University Women some of the leaders among research workers in this country, and we are exceedingly proud of what we have been able to accomplish through Mr. Berliner's vision and generosity.

"It should be remembered that Mr. Berliner made this fellowship available when woman's position in colleges and universities was far from being so assured as now, and when their power to conduct research in any field was questioned. His faith has,

I believe, through the Sarah Berliner Fellowship, encouraged many women to high endeavor and has enheartened them to pursue their interest in science in spite of an atmosphere of what was as recently as eighteen years ago almost universal discouragement.''*

Berliner, of course, is radiantly optimistic with regard to the future possibilities of the inventions with which his name is indissolubly linked—the telephone, the gramophone and radio. Literally, he considers those possibilities illimitable, and progress in their realization, Berliner predicts will be rapid beyond all popular expectation

The Bell Telephone System in 1926 had to increase its share capitalization to one billion one hundred million dollars—making it the largest corporation in the world—to keep pace with the increased growth of telephony.

---

*SARAH BERLINER RESEARCH AND LECTURE FELLOWSHIP

Year	Recipient of Award	University	Selected Subject
1909	Caroline McGill	Missouri	Anatomy
1911	Edna Carter	Vassar	Physics
1912	Gertrude Rand	Bryn Mawr	Biology
1913	Elizabeth R. Laird	Mt. Holyoke	Physics
1914	Ethel N. Browne	Columbia	Biology
1915	Janet T. Howell	Bryn Mawr	Physics
1916	Mildred West Loring	Johns Hopkins	Psychology
1917	Carlotta J. Maury	Hastings-on-Hudson	Paleantology
1918	{ Marjorie O'Donnell	New York	{ Geology
	Cornelia Kennedy	Minnesota	Nutrition
1919	Olive Swezy	Minnesota	Parasitology
1920	Mrs. Helene Connet Wilson	Baltimore	Physiology
1921	Francis G. Wick	Various Colleges	Physics, lumina
1922	Ruth B. Howland	Various Colleges	Biology
1923	Helen C. Coombs	Yonkers	Physiology
1924	Leonora Neuffer	Cincinnati	Chemistry
1925	Hope Hibbard	Various Colleges	Zoology
1926	Helen Downes	Various Colleges	Chemistry

It was only in 1926, too, that the medical world was electrified by news head-lined in the metropolitan journals of the country as follows: "Talking Machine Disks Trap Heart Beats." Then it was narrated that *for the first time in the history of medical science the sound of heart beats was, recorded on talking-machine records* and reproduced for a class of physicians. A hundred doctors from all parts of the United States and from Canada gathered at the Massachusetts General Hospital in Boston on June eighth and listened simultaneously through individual stethoscopes to heart beats engraved on talking-machine records. The sounds were recorded and reproduced in so minute detail that they served for study in diagnosis. The invention is expected to be of far-reaching significance to both the medical profession and the general public. The recording and reproducing devices were developed by Doctor Richard C. Cabot, of Boston, noted physician and educator, and Doctor Clarence Gamble, of Philadelphia, and the results crown eighteen years of study and experimentation.

Radio, in Berliner's judgment, will revolutionize the future art of oratory. It will divest public speaking of the purely flamboyant and clothe it with a dignity born not so much of emotion-stirring eloquence as of conviction-carrying statement of fact and presentation of argument.

"My views on this score," says Berliner, "were put more forcefully than I could express them when

Vice-President Dawes spoke at Washington on June 4, 1926, at the 'finals' of the third national oratorical contest of the high school children of the United States.

" 'The radio,' Mr. Dawes pointed out, 'has interposed itself between the orator and our largest crowds—crowds which run into millions in number—while the exceptional human voice unaided by this device can make itself heard at best by only from five to twenty thousand people. But a fact of immense significance is that each man of the larger number listening to an orator over the radio listens as an individual thinking man and not as one of an impressionable crowd. As scientists have pointed out, when a gathering of people is in the physical presence of an orator and under the spell of his eloquence and personal magnetism, the emotions can be so aroused as not only to interfere with individual mental activity, but at times absolutely to destroy it. The amalgamation of people into crowds seems to create a living organism possessing a definite character and definite mental attributes, one of which is the almost total lack of reasoning power. All this means that instead of reaching the mind through the emotions, a man speaking over the radio must reach the emotions through the mind, if he is to reach them at all. It means that the orator of the future, to hold and impress his audience, must largely abandon appeal to emotion and confine himself to reason forcibly expressed and logically arranged. *It means inevitably that the oratory of the future is to be the oratory of condensed reason, as distinguished from demagoguery with its appeals to prejudice and emotion.* This fact is fraught with tremendous significance to the future public welfare.' "

For whatever good fortune has come to Emile Berliner in a life of constructive contribution to civilization, he gives devout and humble thanks to the spirit of America. In our land of untrammeled opportunity he found himself. From out of its boundless possibilities, with a confidence born of his own experience, he foreshadows that still greater things will come for the enrichment not only of the country of his adoption, but for the world which it leads.

In honor of a friend, who was celebrating a seventieth birthday anniversary, Emile Berliner, contemplating the inevitable fate of mortals, once drew a fantastic picture of the eventide of men and women who have played worthily the rôles assigned them on Life's fitful stage. He wrote this finale:

"And when the end cometh they shall walk down a flower-bedecked slope and meet the smiling old ferryman at the foot of the hill who will beckon them to follow him to the blissful abodes, where dwell the serene and gentle souls that preceded them, into the realms of peace, to the glades where fairies sing enchanting melodies, into a world of sunlit golden dreams.

"There they shall listen to the music of the spheres filling all with their bewitching harmonies. Time has lost its measure and its meaning, space is pierced by the spiritual eye.

"And, beholding a world of splendor and of glories, from the watch towers of eternity, glistening in the tremulous rays of celestial fires, they shall hear the far cry of a venerable Muezzin:

"'Peace be with you, fighting is over, and all is well!'"

THE END

APPENDICES

I

BERLINER'S CAVEAT DESCRIBING THE MICROPHONE*

Filed in the United States Patent Office, April 14, 1877

SPECIFICATION

PART I. The following is a description of my newly-invented apparatus for transmitting sound of any kind by means of a wire or any other conductor of electricity, to any distance.

It is a fact and a scientific principle that objects near each other which are charged with electricity of the same polarity repel each other. It is also a fact that if at a point of contact between two ends of a galvanic current, the pressure between both sides of the contact becomes weakened, the current passing becomes less intense, as, for instance, if an operator on a Morse instrument does not press down the key with a certain firmness, the sounder at the receiving instrument does work much weaker than if

---

*See page 90.

the full pressure of the hand would have been used. Based on these two facts I have constructed a simple apparatus for transmitting sound along a line of a galvanic current in the following manner:

Part II. In the drawing accompanying this *caveat* B is a metal plate well fastened to the wooden box or frame A, but able to vibrate if sound is uttered against it or in the neighborhood of said plate. Against the plate, and touching it, is the metal ball C, which rests on the bar or stand F and presses against the plate, which pressure however can be regulated by the thumb-screw D attached to the ball. By making the plate vibrate the pressure at the point of contact A becomes weaker or stronger as often as vibrations occur and according to which side of the plate the sound comes from.

Part III. If a current of electricity passes through the plate and the point of contact or vice versa, a repulsive movement will take place between the plate and the ball because both are charged with the same kind of electricity. This force of repulsion may be weakened or strengthened by varying the strength of the current.

Part IV. By placing now, as in the drawing is shown, one such instrument in the station fig. 1 and another instrument in the station fig. 2 both situated on the same voltaic current (as shown by the wire connections following the arrows), sound uttered against the plate of the instrument fig. I will be reproduced by the plate of the instrument fig. 2;

for as the vibrations of the transmitter fig.1 caused by the sound will alternately weaken and strengthen the current as many times as vibrations occur, so will also the force of repulsion at the point in the receiver be alternately weakened and strengthened as many times accordingly and will therefore cause the plate to vibrate at the same rate and measure. The latter vibrations being communicated to the surrounding air, the same kind of sound as uttered against the transmitter fig. 1 will be reproduced at the receiver fig. 2, or in as many other receiving instruments as are situated within the same voltaic circuit.

Part V. It is not material that the plate should be of metal; same can be of any material able to vibrate if only at the point of contact suitable arrangement is made so that the current passes through that point. The plate may be of any shape or size and may be substituted by a wire. The ball too may be substituted by any other metallic point, surface, wire, etc. There may be more than one point of contact becoming affected by the same vibrations, and either side or both may vibrate, although it is preferable that only one side should vibrate.

Part VI. If the uttered sound is so strong that its vibrations will cause a breaking of the current at the point or points of contact in the transmitter, then the result at the receiving instruments will be a tone much louder but not as distinct in regard to articulation.

Part VII. What I claim to have invented is,—

1. An instrument situated within an electric circuit having two or more ends of the current brought in contact with each other, which points of contact can be loosened or tightened by vibrating one or both sides of each contact, thus diminishing and increasing the amount of electricity passing through the contacts as many times as vibrations occur.

2. An instrument like this one described situated within a voltaic circuit and having two or more ends of this circuit brought in contact with each other, at which point or points of contact exists a force of repulsion, caused by equal polarity, which force can be increased or decreased by increasing or decreasing the strength of the current passing through the points of contact.

3. An apparatus consisting of a metal plate able to vibrate in contact with a metal ball, each of which within the same voltaic or galvanic circuit, so that if, by vibrating the plate, the pressure at the point of contact gets loosened or tightened, the amount of electricity passing in the current is diminished or increased, as described.

4. Same instrument to be used as a transmitter of sound-waves, by uttering sound against or in the neighborhood of the said plate or its mechanical equivalent, thus vibrating the plate and diminishing the amount of electricity passing as many times and as much as the vibrations will loosen the pressure of contact, as described.

5. Such a similar apparatus to be used as a receiver or reproducer of sound-waves by allowing an electric current consisting of waves which are produced as described in Claim No. 4 to pass through the point of contact thus increasing or decreasing the force of repulsion already existing between the plate and the ball at the contact when a current is passing. The plate therefore being thrown into vibrations as many times and with an intensity in accordance with the number of waves and their intensity, the air surrounding the receiving plates will also be vibrated and reproduce a sound similar to the one uttered in the transmitting instrument, as described.

6. A combination of two or more of such instruments situated on the same voltaic circuit or current of electricity so that if one plate is vibrated all the others will vibrate at the same rate and measure, as described.

7. A system of telephony for the purpose of transmitting sounds to any distance by means of a wire or other conductor of electricity, as described.

II

FINAL DEVELOPMENT OF THE BLAKE TRANSMITTER

[Prepared for the Archives of the American Telephone and Telegraph Company]

IN November, 1878, I left Washington and proceeded to New York, where the Bell Telephone Company had temporary headquarters at Nos. 66 and 68 Reade Street, sharing a loft with the Edison Phonograph Company. The personnel of our company there consisted of Mr. Vail, Mr. Devonshire and myself. Mr. Watson, Mr. Thomas Sanders, the Treasurer of the Company, also Mr. Hubbard, would occasionally come down from Boston to confer with Mr. Vail.

Mr. Francis Blake, Jr., who had invented an ingenius modification of the loose contact transmitter, was at work in Boston trying to put his transmitter into practical commercial form, but he was hampered in his work by an increasing nervousness and he soon afterward retired to his country place, near Newton, where he had fitted up a complete shop and laboratory for the pursuit of scientific research.

314

On January 31, 1879, the Bell Company gave up the office on Reade Street and we all proceeded to Boston. I was requested to take up the perfecting of the Blake transmitter, and the facilities in the shops of Mr. Charles Williams, Jr., who at that time manufactured our instruments, were placed at my disposal. Mr. W. L. Richards was assigned to me as assistant and a very small room had been boarded off on the office floor to serve as a testing station.

The status of the Blake transmitter, when I took hold of it, was briefly, that they could not make twelve transmitters alike good and when these were adjusted at night they were out of adjustment the next morning. Besides this circumstance the quality of transmission was likely to be "boomy" and the transmitter had to be spoken into with care in order that speech be universally well understood at the receiving end. In fact, it took a trained man, one who could judge the transmission by his own receiver, to make commercial talking possible. Such a transmitter could not be sent out for use by telephone subscribers and for a time during 1879 large magneto box telephones, screwed against the wall, continued to be used as transmitters in our telephone service.

The first thing which I discovered was that the platinum bead which formed one contact electrode in the Blake transmitter would, when vibrated by the voice, quickly dig a small cavity into the carbon button which formed the other contact electrode. I proceeded to study the electric-arc light carbon rods from which the buttons were cut. They came from Wallace and Sons, of Ansonia, Connecticut, and were of a beautiful even grain, but soft in quality. We asked one of the Wallace firm to come and see us, and I questioned him if they could not furnish us with carbon rods of a hard quality. He said that it would mean longer baking and this would cause cracks and fissures to develop all through the rods. Success in that direction, therefore, appeared to be doomed to failure.

It then occurred to me that inasmuch as a very hard and dense gas carbon formed in city gas retorts on the inner walls, by slow deposition, why couldn't we have such deposits formed on our soft carbon buttons after they had been cut and finished. It did not take long to design and have made a small cage of steel rods which were far enough apart to permit a free access to any gas but close enough to prevent the carbon buttons from dropping out of the cage. Several dozen of carbon buttons were placed in the cage and, with an introduction to the superintendent of the Boston Gas Works, I proceeded to their plant. I was told that city gas was made in "charges" of four hours each, after which the residual coke was removed and a fresh charge of coal put into the retort. I was also told that the gas was the densest on the top of the coal charge. I requested that my little cage should be placed on the top of the coal during three consecutive charges and that I would send for it the following day. When I received the cage and opened it I found my carbon buttons all shriveled up by heat, and instead of a nice, smooth and hard carbon coating, they had a porous and rough appearance; it looked like failure. But I rubbed one of the shriveled buttons on a piece of emery cloth and, after rubbing off the spongy outer coating, I suddenly found the carbon so hard that the emery would not touch it. I quickly concluded that what had happened was that the gas in the retort had penetrated the carbon buttons while they were red-hot and thereby had hardened them, and that herein I would find the solution of the trouble with the carbon electrodes. A larger and stronger cage was made, several hundred fresh carbon buttons were placed in it and the cage was sent to the gas works with the request that it be placed in the retort for one charge only and be put lower down into the mass of fresh coal. My surmise was found to be correct. The surfaces of these carbon buttons were barely injured and when received were in fine hard shape, ready to be polished after they had been put into their brass casings.

That process remained the standard method of treating the carbon buttons as long as Blake transmitters were manufactured.

My next problem was to purify the sound of the transmission and to prevent the "boomy" quality.

The transmitter diaphragm was at that time held in position by two curved steel springs opposite each other and pressing the loose rubber rimmed dia-phragm against the iron casting which formed the frame that held the transmitter parts. I found that by removing one of the springs and substituting for it a small clip which pressed against the soft rubber rim at the edge of the diaphragm the sound was improved. Furthermore, by reducing the curv-ature of the other spring the transmission became entirely pure. As a final step I straightened the two small springs which held the carbon and the plati-num electrodes so that these springs were parallel with the diaphragm.

After reporting that the Blake transmitter had been perfected, orders were given that two hundred transmitters a day should be made for us. These were tested by myself and Mr. Richards and, once adjusted, they remained in first-class working order. I personally tested the first twenty thousand trans-mitters and then turned this branch of the instru-ments over to Mr. Richards. I devoted myself there-after to research work and helped Professor Charles R. Cross, of the Massachusetts Institute of Technology, in the exhaustive experiments which he made for Mr. Storrow to support the latter's legal work in the defense of our patents and in our attacks against infringers.

The perfected Blake transmitter proved to be vastly superior to the Edison compressed lampblack button transmitter, which the Gold and Stock Tele-graph Company put out for use by its subscribers.

And this, I believe, was an important factor and helped the Bell Company to defeat the Western Union Telegraph Company, bringing the latter to terms which ended the costly telephone fight between the two corporations. It insured to the Bell Company the telephone monopoly.

III

A TRIBUTE TO EMILE BERLINER

ON THE occasion of his seventy-fifth birthday (May 20, 1925) we, the colleagues of Emile Berliner on the Board of Directors of the Association for the Prevention of Tuberculosis of the District of Columbia, in monthly session assembled, wish to offer our felicitations to Mr. Berliner upon his attainment of threescore and fifteen years.

We rejoice in his full possession of the rare gift of mental and physical vigor which he has sought to bring to others, especially the younger generation.

As a constant observer of the Association's twelve *Health Rules,* which he was so largely instrumental in having drafted, Mr. Berliner is particularly an exemplar to all of us in the practise of the precept twelve, "Cultivate cheerfulness and kindliness, it will help you to resist disease." Surely, if that is the secret of Mr. Berliner's *"Mens Sana in Corpore Sano,"* we shall wish to thank him for showing us the way of eternal youth.

No one but the Recording Angel will ever know the number of infant and child lives saved in this community by Mr. Berliner's tireless efforts to obtain for Washington a safe commercial milk supply.

Ever since 1901 and before the movement against tuberculosis was organized, as we know it to-day, Mr. Berliner in season and out of season has preached the danger of raw milk, especially in the feeding of infants and invalids. After a quarter of a century of such efforts, Mr. Berliner had the satisfaction of seeing Congress clothe the health officer with power to regulate milk standards in the District of Columbia, a policy which he so long and untiringly advocated.

Mr. Berliner's interest in health education and his belief in the value of publicity and reiteration of health precepts in the public press and through the printed page are too well-known to his colleagues of this Association to call for extended remarks. In the minutes of the monthly meetings of the Board of Directors the reports of the Chairman of the Committee on Publications bear permanent testimony to Mr. Berliner's efforts to spread the gospel of positive health.

We, the directors of this Association, congratulate ourselves upon having had as our president from 1917 to 1922, and as a charter member of the Association, Emile Berliner, whose inventions have brought happiness and satisfaction to countless thousands, as well as honor, fame and world-wide recognition to himself from fellow-scientists; a man whose devotion to public health and public welfare has not been second in interest to his scientific attainments.

322 EMILE BERLINER

RESOLVED: That a copy of this tribute be placed upon the permanent records of the Association for the Prevention of Tuberculosis of the District of Columbia and an engrossed copy be presented to Mr. Berliner with the assurance of the esteem and affection of his colleagues of the Board of Directors of the Association.

George M. Kober, M. D.
President

Attest
Walter S. Ufford
Seal   Secretary
May 10, 1926

IV

A SPECIMEN OF BERLINER'S "HEALTH EDUCATION" BULLETINS

How a Love Kiss May Be a Death Kiss

(FROM THE WASHINGTON STAR)

AMONG my acquaintances is a young couple, who, at the time of the occurrence which I will relate, had a beautiful five-months-old boy baby, well developed physically, and particularly bright and winsome. One day the child appeared to have caught a catarrhal cold. The next day it developed a fever temperature, pneumonia set in, and on the following morning the child died.

With the sadness of the event on my mind, I attempted to find out, if possible, where the child caught the infection that killed it. From the father I learned that the apartment in which they lived was cleaned with vacuum cleaners, that their rooms were swept with carpet sweepers, that they were careful at all times to have good ventilation, and that watchful intelligence prevailed in their home in order to have it sanitary and well lighted.

During the funeral, which I attended, I heard the mother of the child repeatedly cough in a way which indicated that she had a bad bronchial affection, and when the carriages had returned it occurred to me to ask the father if, to his knowledge, the child had ever been kissed on the mouth by anybody. He said no, that they never had allowed anybody to kiss the baby, and only Katherine, the mother, occasionally had kissed it, and then, of course, on the mouth.

Needless to say, I forbade the father ever to tell his wife that I had questioned him, but I warned him that if there should be another child that he should see to it that no one, not even the mother, should ever kiss it on the mouth. I explained to him how such a kiss on the lips of a child, with its delicate mucous membranes and its low resistance to disease, might easily set up and develop an infection of dangerous proportion, even though the pathogenic or disease germs that could produce infection in a child might in the mouth of a healthy adult remain harmless.

It was the late General George M. Sternberg, for a number of years surgeon-general of the United States Army and a scientist of great distinction and repute, who first discovered germs of pneumonia in the sputum of a great many adults who were otherwise in perfect health. He found the germ (known as the pneumo-coccus) even in his own mouth, and also other germs, resting latent and without danger, but ready to set up serious infections should the carrier of the germs have had his natural resistance to disease lowered. Such a state might be brought about by various hygienic omissions, by the continuous breathing of bad air, by the continuous partaking of impure food, notably raw milk and cream; by excesses of all kinds, by morbid thoughts and by lack of cheer and kindliness.

When body resistance is thus lowered, pathogenic or disease-producing germs may rapidly multiply in the highly favorable environments of the warm inner mouth, or oral cavity, and invade the human organism, causing disease. That is the accepted theory of general infection. Even of greater import than the disease germ itself is the ready soil on which it may grow and multiply. This is what we must guard against, and progressive and specific hygiene teaches us how to do so.

The warning which the above occurrence carries need not unduly alarm healthy adults, nor young lovers with their splendid vitality, nor members of families in good condition of health. It need not necessarily impugn the safety of all demonstrations of deep affection between humankind.

But it does most strongly apply to children, who, on account of their frailness of bodies and the delicate kind of tissue forming their mucous membranes, are very sensitive to infection. It also applies to those adults who are for a time in an undermined condition of health, in a state of lessened resistance to disease, which happens now and then in every one's life.

Former Surgeon-General Doctor Rupert Blue

told me at the time of the last influenza epidemic that he gargled twice a day with a good antiseptic solution in order to destroy such pathogenic germs as might have got and lodged in his mouth or throat. He said that if this was done by everybody at regular intervals a large amount of preventable disease would be nipped in the bud before endangering health.

There are many antiseptic solutions to be had, some of which are more or less efficacious in destroying disease germs. And recently a pathological laboratory in Washington tested a solution made, according to my doctor's prescription, as follows:

Menthol .... 4 grains
Alcohol .... 1 ounce
Sod. Bicarb .... 30 grains
Sod. Borate .... 30 grains
Dist. water .... 8 ounces
    Filter if necessary.

It was found to be a true and rather high-grade germicide. This solution, which can be had from any druggist, is cheap, and I personally have found it most efficacious as a gargle or a spray for many years. Even when diluted with water in fifty-fifty proportion, it will, when promptly applied several times at short intervals, break up a fresh sore throat or it will correct an infected or badly tasting mouth, provided the cause is not in the teeth or in the stomach.

sand per second, we receive the sensation of a chord, or of a single mass of sound, either of harmony or disharmony.

This is similar to the manner in which the eye receives a motion picture, by the rapid projection of several progressive photographs of a moving object. Even if we listen to a whole orchestra, with or without the addition of singing, the ear at one instant only takes notice of that fraction of the performance which happens at that moment to predominate.

To prove that this is the case we can let sound write itself down by means of the phonautograph, invented by the Frenchman, Leon Scott, about 1856.

One of these instruments is in the United States National Museum. It consists of a large cylinder, covered with paper, the surface of which is covered with soot from a smoky flame. A sound box, having a diaphragm and a receiving horn, is provided with a slender bristle stylus, fastened to the center of the diaphragm, and which is so adjusted that the stylus just touches the surface of the cylinder sidewise. When the cylinder is rotated and passes the stylus in screw fashion the latter traces a spiral line around the cylinder.

If now sound is emitted into the horn the spiral line becomes waves and each wave represents a fraction of the sound that caused the diaphragm to vibrate.

It will then be found that the higher pitched the sound is, the more rapidly do these waves follow one another, and as the pitch is lower the fewer are the waves in a given time. In the case of an orchestra playing, the wave line becomes most complicated, yet there is discernible a certain regularity, as sets of waves repeat themselves when a more or less sustained chord is recorded.

Jazz effects will record themselves in waves of striking or irregular forms and so will all mere noises which in themselves are not considered musical.

If we try to analyze the wave lines of articulate speech by means of a phonautograph we shall discern sets of complicated waves which represent the vowel sounds, but most consonants, like *r, s, sh, c,* and *z,* which are very minute waves, repeating themselves rapidly.

The tune or melody is due to the inspiration of the composer, but the harmony to accompany the tune follows strict laws, which, while capable of a great variety of modulations, must be kept within certain limits, prescribed by the science of harmony. The highest musical art is expressed by proper orchestration, and the finest compositions are those in which the inspiration of a lovely or artistic melody proceeds and stands out against the background of perfect harmony, expressed by skilful orchestration. Such is the case for instance in so-called grand opera. Besides, we have the works of orchestral music itself, with an infinite variety of leading melodies, as well as the masterpieces of dramatic effects giving the musical background by means of which stage action is illuminated or by which emotions are expressed. Then there are the immortal creations of piano and organ music, instrumental and vocal duets, trios, quartettes and sextettes, and the superb compositions for the violin and other solo instruments. Songs of all kinds from the simple folk melodies to the great church masses and oratories form a rich heritage bestowed on us by past geniuses, and which are added to without end by living creations of contemporaneous songs and harmonies.

All these treasures of musical science have during the past twenty years been made more accessible to the great public by the talking machine. In this instrument the record is not merely a wave line drawn on paper, but is a groove of sound waves indented, engraved or etched into solid material. The sound waves are either represented by the varying depths of a straight groove, as in the phonograph and graphophone, or by a groove looking like the old phonautographic record, of even depth, and showing the sound waves as an undulating groove writing. The latter system is that of the Gramophone or Victrola and is the more perfect of the two, so that the great singers and performers prefer that their art be recorded by that system.

Sound is reproduced in talking machines because the sound grooves move the stylus connected with the center of the diaphragm and the latter is vibrated by the sound waves that are embodied in the grooves caused by the original sound waves.

Like engravings for printing, sound records can be duplicated without limit by pressing electrotyped reverse engravings, called matrices, into a proper material under heat and pressure. The material usually employed is a special kind of hard black sealing wax, so that a disk sound record might often be properly called the seal of the human voice.

VI

WONDERS

An Essay

(WRITTEN ABOUT 1890 BY EMILE BERLINER)

PEOPLE are apt to look for wonders in the sphere of the supernatural, in the narrative of the Holy Scriptures, in the fables of antiquity, and in the seances of so-called spiritualism, but by far the greatest wonders are every-day occurrences and lie around in innumerable forms in our immediate neighborhood. Let me cite a few.

Here is a piece of glass. It is of so dense a material that the most rarified gases, which would easily pass through a block of brass or steel, can be held forever within a bulb of glass, the walls of which are less than a hundredth of an inch thick. Yet all the vibrations of light emanating from the various objects of a landscape will pass unobstructed through a pane several inches thick, permitting the picture to be accurately represented on the retina of our eye, and even a block of several feet thickness would still permit a fair view through it of the forms and colors behind.

Take a magnet and a mounted needle of iron, put
between both a granite block weighing several tons,
and the needle will still obey the motion of the magnet, just as if the granite block did not exist.

You may pass an electric current strong enough
to kill by shock a dozen oxen at once, or to set in motion machinery representing a thousand horsepower,
through a small bar of copper; but this very bar of
copper will not alter its weight while the current is
passing, nor show any outward indication whatever
of the tremendous force pulsating through it.

A piece of musk may exhale its penetrating odor
in a large hall with open windows for ten years,
but it would require a very delicate balance to prove
that it has lost in weight from the expenditure of so
much odoriferous energy.

A violin is perfectly tuned by the harmony resulting from one tone and the fifth following on the
regular scale, but if a piano would be tuned on the
same principle, i. e., that every fifth tone would
make a perfect harmony with the first, the piano,
even if played by a Rubinstein or a Liszt, would
give out such fearful discords as to drive away the
cats beyond hearing distance.

A square and a circle are each a most perfect
geometrical form endowed with wonderful possibilities in the hands of a skilled mathematician, yet it
is impossible mathematically to calculate from a circle a square which would represent the same surface
of area as the circle, or vice versa. The assumed
diameter of a circle always lacks a fraction.

At a distance of several miles let us place a number of candles, the tallow of which has been mixed each with a different substance, for instance, salt, iron dust, potassium, niter, etc. There will be apparently no difference in the kind or amount of light shown by each candle, nor would a powerful telescope reveal such, but upon looking at the flames with a small triangular block of glass called a prism, and which is suitably mounted, we can at once determine what substance has been mixed with each stick of tallow. Based upon this wonder we are able to determine the composition of burning stars many billions of miles away.

If a wire be stretched five times around the earth, an electric current would traverse it in one second, and a person killed by lightning hasn't time enough left to see the flash.

A puff of air not strong enough to extinguish a candle flame, when slowly blown across the mouth of a glass bottle will produce a tone loud enough to be heard several hundred feet; and at Cabin John's Bridge, near Washington, a soft whisper will travel from end to end under the arch which stretches about two hundred and fifty feet, and is seventy-five feet high. It seems incredible that a whisper would have that much penetrating power.

The laws of gravitation are so perfect that they enabled Leverrier to predict the discovery, and point out the exact position in the heavens, of the planet Neptune, which was found there a few days later, and which is two billion, six hundred million miles away from the sun.

The power of the brain to recall by memory the impressions received by us years ago is beyond doubt one of the greatest wonders, and is likely forever to remain an unfathomable mystery.

The heart beats forty million times in a year, and the lungs inhale seven hundred thousand gallons of air in the same period, and all this and a great many other functions of the human body, one more elaborate that the other, continue without undue friction and disturbance—unless it be by our own trespasses—for seventy years, and all that is required for us to do is to eat and drink the good things of earth; for the rest of the organs of the body take care of themselves.

Thus, and through countless other wonders, by teaching humility to its disciples, Science assumes the rôle of a most potent religion.

INDEX

INDEX

INDEX

339